Go Tell It
on the Mountain

Go Tell It
on the Mountain

compiled and edited by
Jackie Johnson Maughan

STACKPOLE
BOOKS

Copyright © 1996 by Stackpole Books

Published by
STACKPOLE BOOKS
5067 Ritter Road
Mechanicsburg, PA 17055

Printed in the United States of America

10 9 8 7 6 5 4 3 2 1

First edition

Reprint permissions noted on page 209.

Library of Congress Cataloging-in-Publication Data

Go tell it on the mountain / [compiled by] Jackie Johnson Maughan.—1st ed.
   p.   cm.
  ISBN 0-8117-0738-5 (hc)
  1. Fire lookouts—West (U.S.)—Anecdotes. 2. Fire lookout stations—West (U.S.)—Anecdotes. I. Maughan, Jackie Johnson. 1948–
SD421.375.G6   1996
634.9′618′0973—dc20   95-32616
                                        CIP

In Memory: The Storm King Fire Fighters

Kathi Beck, Tami Bickett, Scott Blecha, Levi Brinkley, Robert Browning, Doug Dunbar, Terri Ann Hagen, Bonnie Jean Holtby, Robert A. Johnson, Jon R. Kelso, Don Mackey, Roger Roth, Jim Thrash, and Richard Tyler

CONTENTS

Introduction

I WENT UP on my first fire lookout in 1992 because I wanted to finish a novel I was working on. I was thinking about how writers such as Norman Maclean and Jack Kerouac and Edward Abbey had sought this isolation; and how, in fact, there was actually a tradition of fire lookout writing going back to Maclean's story "USFS 1919: The Ranger, the Cook, and a Hole in the Sky."

I would seek this isolation and its peculiar vulnerability because that's what I needed—three months alone with the people and events of my novel. Well, the novel didn't get written (at least not then), because, first, the nature of fire watch has changed, and second, the people and events of that first fire season and subsequent ones filled my mind. What happened instead is the book you have in your hands.

A fire lookout is often not quiet. It's not like the old days when, if you saw a fire, you could ring up the ranger station on the hand-crank telephone and report it. Instead, nowadays we have radios. This is much more convenient and efficient, but it also means noise—lots of it during a busy fire season, and the lookout from atop her or his particular perch hears much of it. Most of it has nothing to do with the lookout's business, and some may wonder what we do all day with "nothing to do."

The summer of 1994 I was on a lookout in eastern Oregon, not too far from the small town of Prineville, home of the Prineville Hot Shots. As their name implies, Hot Shots are among the elite of backcountry fire fighters. But nine of these young men and women were now dead, caught days earlier in a blowup on the Storm King Fire in Colorado. The fatalities numbered fourteen in all, with three smoke jumpers and two helitack included. It is not my purpose to analyze why some of our bravest and best were taken in that fire, but rather to point out that sometimes the "noise" on the radio is deadly serious. And it is to these fire fighters and their families and those of us who try to watch over them that this book is dedicated.

As you will see from the essays and fiction included here, most fire lookouts find the occupation itself so compelling that if they write, this is what they write about. That's what happened to me. In putting this book together, I tried to draw from writing both past and present. The more recent material was solicited by a massive mailing to present and former fire lookouts throughout the nation. What I decided to include is from the West, where most of the still-active lookouts are stationed.

In the 1950s, the heyday of fire lookouts, there were probably six thousand; now the number is down to six hundred or so, and many of these are going fast. There is also a disturbing trend to staff lookouts with volunteers. Although fire watch isn't work in the nine-to-five sense, it certainly is responsibility, and pinpointing a fire accurately or not going stir-crazy or not freaking out in a lightning storm is something that should be rewarded in the monetary, as well as the spiritual, sense.

Being a fire lookout is a spiritual experience, and a number of the writings included here address this point. My editors at Stackpole, Judith Schnell and Mark Allison, did the arranging of the essays, and to quote Mark, "It would work best to have a good mix: a longer, more philosophical piece followed by a lighter, more humorous piece. This would keep the reader moving forward and reflect the flow, the randomness of the firewatcher's day."

And the days do stretch long and time really does seem to slow, and one is often sated with silence, an experience, I believe, that is becoming rarer, more precious and more valuable. One of my motives was and still is to taste the contemplative life, to enter the cloister of the wilderness—as Thomas Merton, poet, essayist, and Trappist monk for twenty-seven years until his death in 1967, put it so beautifully in his book *The Seven Storey Mountain,* "to walk out of the miseries of the world and into a refuge of my own choosing."

Jackie Johnson Maughan

Fire Lookout

Edward Abbey

MEN GO MAD in this line of work. Read a book called *The Dharma Bums* by Jack Kerouac and you'll see what I mean. He spent a summer as fire lookout in a shack on Sourdough Mountain in the Cascades, a lookout haunted by the spirit of Gary "Japhy Ryder" Snyder who had also worked there. Kerouac never recovered. A few years later the Forest Service offered me the same job at the same place. Trying to maintain their literary reputation. Prudently I turned it down.

Women too go mad in the solitary confinement of a mountain peak, though not so readily as men, being stronger, more stable creatures, with a lower center of gravity. Perhaps the severest test of a marriage is to assign a man and wife to a fire lookout; any couple who survive three or four months with no human company but each other are destined for a long, permanent relationship. They deserve it.

My career as a fire lookout began by chance. Having injured my knee during the Vietnam War (skiing in Colorado), I was unable to resume my usual summer job as patrol ranger in a certain notorious Southwestern national park. I requested a desk job. The Chief Ranger thought I lacked the competence to handle government paper work. He offered me instead the only job in the Park which required less brains, he said, than janitor, garbage collector or Park Superintendent. He made me fire lookout on what is called the North Rim, a post so remote that there was little likelihood I'd either see or be seen by the traveling American public. An important consideration, he felt.

The lookout tower on North Rim was sixty feet tall, surmounted by a little tin box six feet by six by seven. One entered through a trapdoor in the bottom. Inside was the fire finder—an azimuth and sighting device—fixed to a cabinet bolted to the floor. There was a high swivel chair with glass insulators, like those on a telephone line, mounted on the lower tips of the chair's four legs. In case of lightning. It was known as the electric chair. The actual operations of a fire lookout, quite simple, I have described elsewhere.

My home after working hours was an old cabin near the foot of the tower. The cabin was equipped with a double bed and a couple of folding steel cots, a wood-burning stove, table, shelves, cupboard, two chairs. It made a pleasant home, there under the pines and aspen, deep in the forest, serenaded by distant coyote cries, by poor wills, and sometimes by the song of the hermit thrush, loveliest of bird calls in the American West.

My father came to visit one day and stayed for the season. He was given the job of relief lookout on my days off. In the evenings after supper we played horseshoes. Whenever I hear the jangle of horseshoes now I think of North Rim, of that forest, that cabin, that summer. My father has powerful hands, hard, gnarled, a logger's hands, very large. In his hand a playing horseshoe looks like a quoit; a horse's shoe can hardly be seen at all. His pitch is low and accurate, the shoe—open end forward—sliding with a soft *chunk* full upon the upright, rigid peg. A firm connection. Top that ringer, son, he'd say. We walked the Grand Canyon from rim to rim that summer, and once again a few years ago. The second time he was seventy-two years old.

The first sensible thing I did at North Rim, before my father appeared, was fall in love with the ranger. Not the Chief Ranger but the one who manned the park entrance station a few miles down the road. Park Ranger Hendrickson (GS-4) was one of those golden Californians from the San Diego area. She wore her sea-bleached hair in a heavy ponytail that fell below her clavicles. Like most girl swimmers she had a well-developed pair of lungs, much admired by the boys. Pretty as a Winesap in September, she looked especially fetching in her ranger suit: broad-brimmed straw hat, white blouse with Park Service pin, the snug skirt of forest green twill that ended, as was the fashion then, a good six inches above her knees. Like most sexual perverts I've always suffered from a fatal weakness for women in uniform— for cheerleaders, majorettes, waitresses, meter maids, prison matrons, etc. On my first meeting with Bonnie Hendrickson (as we shall here name the young woman) I said to her, frankly, "You know—I've always wanted to lift a ranger's skirt."

"You'll need a hiking permit," she replied. A quick-witted girl— with a B.A. in French. We soon became good friends. On my days off

I sometimes helped her get through the tedious hours at the entrance station. While she leaned out her little window collecting entrance fees from the tourists, answering questions, chatting about Smokey the Bear and the fire danger, I was kneeling at her feet, unseen from outside, gently rolling down the ranger's pantyhose. We played various such experiments in self control. I experimented, she displayed the self control. An innocent game, like horseshoes, with similar principles. Top that ringer . . .

On her days off she would visit me in the lookout tower, assisting me in *my* duties. As I'd be reporting a fire over the Park Service radio system she was unbuttoning my Levi's. "Fire Dispatch," I said into the microphone, "this is North Rim Lookout."

"Yeah?" The Fire Dispatcher had the weary, cynical voice of a police desk sergeant. "What's your problem now, Abbey?"

"Reporting a smoke, sir."

"Yeah? And where do you think this one is Abbey?"

"Well sir, I've got a reading of zero-four-two degrees and thirty—oooh, watch those fingernails!—thirty minutes. Near Fredonia."

"Yeah . . ." A long pause. Then the weary voice. "I hate to tell you this, Abbey, but that's the same fire you reported last week. Like I told you then, that's the Fredonia sawmill and it's been smoking away in that same spot for fifty years. Ten four?"

"Yes sir, ten four. Oh Christ . . . oh *yes . . .!*"

"No swearing on the airwaves. These here transmissions are monitored by the Federal Communications Commission."

One cold rainy afternoon Bonnie and I were down in the cabin on the bed, a fire crackling in the stove, when our experiments were interrupted by a banging on the door. Bonnie ducked beneath the covers, I yanked on my pants and cracked the door open. Two Park Service fire fighters stood there grinning at me through the drizzle, their truck snuggled against the plump round rear of Bonnie's little car. "Hey Ed," says one, "we got a report of a hot fire in this area."

"Get out of here." I slammed and barred the door.

But I don't want to give the impression that a fire lookout's life is all work. There was time for play. One night a week we'd drive to the village on the Canyon rim and visit the bar. My Hopi friend would be there, old Sam Banyaca the shaman, and the veteran mule wrangler known only as Walapai, a leathery runt of an Indian cowboy who always squatted on top of his barstool, having never learned to sit on anything but a horse. Behind the bar was Robert the intellectual bar-

tender, smug smirk on his fat face, about to recite a new limerick. He
claimed to be the only living composer of original limericks in America.
I still remember two of them. I wish I could forget.

> A modest young fellow named Morgan
> Had an awesome sexual organ;
> It resembled a log
> Dredged up from a bog,
> With a head on it fierce as a Gorgon.

And the other:

> An old Mormon bishop named Bundy
> Used to wed a new wife every Sunday;
> But his multiple matehood
> Was ruined by statehood—
> *Sic transit gloria* Monday.
> "*Mundi!*"
> "Monday!"

"It's Tuesday, f'crush sake," says old Walapai, turning his bleary eyes
toward us and swaying on his stool. "You honkies drunk already?" He
crashed to the floor.

I spent four sweet summers on that sublime North Rim, not always
alone in my tower. During the third summer a thing happened which
caused me the deepest grief of my life. So far. The pain of my loss
seemed unendurable. I called an old friend, Ann Woodin of Tucson, for
comfort. She came to my part of the forest bearing apples, a flagon,
black caviar and a magnum of Mumm's. We sat on a log under the trees
at evening, by a fire, and listened to the birds, and talked, and ate the
cavier and drank champgane, and talked some more. She helped me
very much. A lady with class, that Ann. A lady *of* class. The same who
once rescued me, at two in the morning, from the Phoenix City Jail
down in Goldwater country, where the police had locked me up for
what they called "negligent driving." Joseph Wood Krutch, another
Tucsonan, dedicated one of his books to Ann Woodin. She is, he
wrote, "an ever-present help in time of trouble."

Four summers. Sweet and bitter, bittersweet hilarious seasons in the
forest of ponderosa and spruce and fir and trembling aspen trees. The
clang of horseshoes in the twilight. The smell of woodsmoke from the
cabin. Deep in the darkling pines the flutesong of a hermit thrush.
Lightning, distant thunder, and clouds that towered into evening. Rain
on the roof in the night.

One day somebody in Park headquarters, down on the South Rim of the Canyon, the bad rim, said to somebody else, "Do we really need a fire lookout on North Rim?"

And the other man said, "I didn't know we had one."

The lookout was closed at the end of my fourth season and has never been used since. My father had long before returned to his own woods in Pennsylvania where he still lives and works. He is now seventy-eight. And Ranger Hendrickson—sweet witty lovely daring Bonnie—she had gone back to California where, I've heard, she married well, to a man with a steady job, property, money, prospects, a head on his shoulders. Not a fire lookout. Not by a long shot.

Listening to Voices in the Wilderness

Nicole LeFavour

IT IS NINE O'CLOCK. The sun is falling behind Big Baldy Mountain to the northwest. The shapes of ridges spread out below me one after another to every horizon—each a different hue, cast in a different light, completely unbroken by the lines of roads or buildings. It takes four-teen hours to hike to the nearest road, three hours more by car to the nearest town. The air is still and warm, and from a lake basin far below the lookout I hear the sound of a branch breaking, perhaps an elk in the trees or a bear turning over a log to find insects. It is that still.

I sit on the green-painted planks of the catwalk. I have slept in the tiny lookout for nearly two months. I hesitate to say I have lived here alone. There is nothing to keep my own internal voice and all the mil-lions of images away. Everything I have ever lived washes in like a tide here between the books I read, the work I do assessing fires, plotting strikes, giving weather reports, and relaying messages on the radio. There is no tape deck, no TV, no movie theater, no telephone, no other real human voice or touch to distract me or keep me from the play of my own life. At this time of night, even the forest radio is silent. It is not possible to avoid thinking. Sometimes I write just to make my mind's occupation more material and real.

I am not surprised that many people cannot bear to be alone in this way. If the thoughts flooding through me here in this silence were all regrets, if there were too much pain or fear, I'd go mad. This is my sec-ond year as a lookout. I have actually come to welcome letting my mind play to itself in the stillness.

I spend my days simply. In the evening I haul water, gather wood, search for mushrooms and berries, explore the drainages that fall from the mountaintop. I cook, sleep, and sharpen tools. I use what I need, basic things. I fix whatever breaks.

Tonight, as the color in the valleys deepens and falls into darkness, no lights break the blanket of ridgetops and valleys. Only stars above, the sky huge.

Ten miles away to the northwest, another lookout, Pat, cooks his supper. To the south, Jody sits perched in a building like mine, illuminated by a gas lamp hung over the wood-burning stove. To the east, far off, Pamela and Meg may already be asleep against the sky. Beyond that is town. I could never have imagined the feeling of being here so far from anyone, in a place so huge and filled with its own cycles of light and wind, death, birth, growth, decay.

Years growing up in this country have shown me that I cannot be here without affecting the rhythms of the day for the animals around me. Years working for the Forest Service have made me all too aware of the changes this country has seen. The decades of lookout use show on the tree stumps and snags below. Every year we have to walk farther for wood, the skeleton of another ancient limber pine turned to a streak of wood smoke stretched across the sky. Every year the helicopter landing pad gets bigger and more elaborate, trees are cut and fire lines dug into the hillside. Every year more people and horses climb the trail to the mountaintop; rocks are turned, lichen scraped, paths widened, tree wells hoofed bare of grass and whortleberry, tree bark rubbed to cambium by tie lines and lead ropes.

I wonder if we have enough wilderness to provide all of us with solitude. Like others, every year I grow more selfish and weary. I leave the names of the most silent places out of my conversations. Sometimes—listening to the flow of airplane after airplane filled with people, finding new campsites and beaten-out lakeshores, or thumbing through the pages of guidebooks inviting all to come enjoy this undiscovered place—I feel a sense of panic.

I have grown strong on this silence, this wilderness. I own none of it, though it is more home for me than anywhere I have ever lived. This is the only place my own life has ever come to me so fully. I have never felt as awake and alive as I do out here.

When I leave, I'll take part of this with me—a feeling or image of myself in a place: in the hanging granite rocks on Tango Ridge; in the ice-covered grass by a small, unnamed lake; in a basin meadow filled with the sound of elk calves crying like dolphins; in the feel of wind in the mountaintops, the smell of sagebrush, wet duff, and wood smoke. Images of places I'll probably never visit again. When I take my things and walk down the mountain behind a string of mules, when I drive down to the city to live and teach, my only possession will be the knowledge that each of these places is here, that they exist.

I sit on the corner of the catwalk, my legs hanging over a thousand feet of darkness. It is warm, but I shiver at the vastness. I pick up my binoculars and go back inside. I close the door, crawl into bed, cover my head with the blankets. It is only after dark that the chaos of all the unknown and unseen crowds in and awe finally approaches fear. Still, I sleep well. The noises beneath the lookout and off in the dark of the trees to the north make me small, keep me humble. No helicopter could fly to rescue me. At best, here at night I can broadcast my voice over the radio into the darkness, disturb the sleep of others curled in lookouts, miles away across rivers, ridges, and mountainsides.

The darkness and vastness out here make morning miraculous. It makes me feel strong, certain I can survive.

I look around at the shapes of mountains warming in the dawn, at what seems to be an immense expanse of wild country, and I think of the millions of human pressures tearing at it. I pick up an old newspaper and read through the headlines. Somewhere far away men and women in the depths of marble buildings debate our need for wilderness. They question whether we should preserve any more of what remains. Listening here on the mountaintop, I worry that we will squander what remains. I worry that already we have not left ourselves enough of it.

The Little Black Cloud

RAY KRESEK

MY FIRE CAREER began on a lookout. It ended on a lookout thirty-five years later. During all the years between, I put out fires for a living, a few thousand of them: fires on the grasslands, fires in the bush, fires in the wilderness forests, fires in manure piles, fires in skyscrapers, houses, airplanes—you name it. Enough fires, I never wanted to see another one. So I went back up on a lookout to end my career—the Heavens Gate lookout in Idaho.

I chose Heavens Gate because it offered the largest variety of Forest Service involvement. It overlooks, from eighty-four hundred feet, three national forests in three U.S. Forest Service Regions: the Nez Perce in Region I, the Payette in Region IV, and the Wallowa-Whitman in Region VI. Each, of course, had its own way of doing things, particularly regarding fire management.

In each corner of the room was a radio. The fourth was my retirement gift, a nice VHF ham radio capable of working much of the world from that elevation. It also permitted me to hear the real story about the huge wildfires that were burning around the Northwest that summer of 1988, from the contract pilots' point of view.

I'd also chosen Heavens Gate for the variety of people I was sure to meet. I lined the walls above the windows with quite an assortment of lookout relics from our Fire Lookout Museum in Spokane and was eager to share the stories about them. Foreign tour guides suggest the visit to America's deepest canyon, Hells Canyon. Of the places in Idaho you can drive to, the best view you can get of the canyon and the Seven Devils is from Heavens Gate. As a result, I had sixteen hundred visitors in '88, coming not only from forty-nine states, but twenty-three nations as well.

It was a bright, sunny day, just a week after we'd opened the lookout for the summer, when I decided it was time to scrape the ugly paint off the door of the propane refrigerator. Some other fire watcher years before had somehow seen fit to cover a little rust on the white porcelain finish by painting the whole door with some leftover gray house paint.

With an elbow resting on the refrigerator top, I was busy with a paint scraper in the other hand. All of a sudden I got a catch in my back and stood straight up. Just as I stood up, a stroke of lightning came right out of the clear blue sky and struck the tower! The sun was still shining, but a little black cloud had developed right above the lookout. I hadn't even seen it.

A ball of fire blew out the back of the refrigerator like an M-80 firecracker. It blinded me for a moment and made my ears ring for days. My faithful German shepherd had been lying on the floor near the refrigerator, and her nose suffered a large blister from the shock. The refrigerator never worked again. Neither did the three Forest Service radios or my brand new $500 ham rig. Two inches of solid half-inch copper antenna on the top of the tower had melted into a puddle. Otherwise, the tower had suffered no damage.

A family from Craigmont, Idaho, had been up for a visit and were standing in the parking lot half a mile away when it happened. They were admiring the tower and were fascinated by a tiny black cloud above it, the only cloud in the sky. To their amazement, a single bolt of lightning dropped out and lit up the tower as it struck the ground. For a few moments they stared, dumbfounded by what they had just seen, certain that I lay dead up in that glass house. Then I walked out on the catwalk to see what the hell had just happened. They waved for the longest time, then got in their car and drove off, with quite a story to tell. (They told me about this on a return visit two weeks later.)

As the tiny cloud moved on, it left a few drops of rain and a rainbow that appeared, from the catwalk, to end in the Heavens Gate lookout rain gauge.

It wasn't yet my time to go.

August Midnight

Martha Hardy

It was midnight on the northwest ridge. The arm of Tatoosh flung out toward Mount Rainier was draped by day in a tricolored sleeve, green for the fringe of trees on the west, brown for the strip of earth on top, white for the ruffle of snow on the edge of the cliff. But at midnight the ridge was swathed in black, unbroken except by the sheen of moonlight on the drifts.

Turning my flashlight on and off in the process of sketching the silhouette of house and peak a quarter of a mile away, I felt oddly conspicuous, seated on the root of a scrub fir in the intermittent glare reflected from sketch pad and snow. It had taken exactly a month to make up my mind to venture out here after dark, but here I was at last, alone except for the hidden wild things that were probably staring at me.

But if the creatures were there, they made no sound. There was nothing to hear except the wind, nothing to see except the shape of the station, the blur of trees, the vast dark bowl of the basin with the little lake lost in the bottom, the glimmering drifts, the pale stars, and a moon almost full but threatened with clouds.

Snow and earth were crisp underfoot, and the air was filled with the breath of sleeping August, the mingled scents of flowers and foliage, cedar, fir and juniper. And since no one except myself knew I was out here, there was all the tang of real adventure in this foray into the very heart of midnight.

I had turned out the flashlight and was searching among the stars for a familiar constellation to use in my sketch, when out of the darkness behind me came a cry so loud and shrill that I jumped up, whirled and dropped the sketch pad on the drift. Then, as the night grew raucous with sounds like yells of boys playing some outlandish game, I knew that coyotes were not far away.

An edge of cloud slid onto the moon, and I shivered in the sudden blackness shot through with the eerie wails of the little yellow wolves. Fumbling for the tree root, I heard a flutter at my feet and realized that the rising wind had found the sketch pad, which was the Lookout's diary with drawing paper clipped to its firm back.

As I turned on the light and reached for the pad, a strong gust whipped over the ridge, snatched the sketches from under the clips, and scooted the book across the glazed surface of the snow. Lunging, I slipped and dropped the flashlight. By the time I found it, the diary was poised on the lip of the cornice, pages flapping like hands waving for help. Before I could take one step, my Lookout's diary, official United States Government document, vital record of one pair of eyes of the Forest Service, was on its way to the bottom of the cliff and perhaps the open water at the west side of the lake.

Slipping and slithering across the glaze, I swung the beam frantically north and south until it picked up a curve of bare earth close to the edge of the cliff. Like mad I made for it, threw myself over a foot-wide rim of snow, and scrambled down a rough bank. Flicking the beam over the cliff face, I saw two sheets of paper fluttering against the wall, and farther down the diary, lodged behind a small rock on a ledge. As another gust whipped the leaves of the book, I knew that every second counted.

Working diagonally down and to the right, more slowly now because holds were harder to find, I reached a position about ten feet above the book with smooth rock beneath my last foothold. Peering down at the ledge I decided it was wide enough to offer safe landing if I should jump.

With my back to the vast emptiness of the basin, I dropped. Landing with a jolt, I tipped over backward, sat down hard, threw out my arms for balance, and felt the flashlight fly out of my hand. There came the crack of it striking the cliff, then silence.

My thoughts were on the vanished torch as I tucked the diary inside my shirt and stood up to consider the situation. From the way my legs were quivering like a chipmunk's tail, the descent must have been steeper than it seemed, and I was suddenly aware that I would not be going back the way I had come. In the light of the flash I had seen no breaks in the smooth rock between the ledge and the last foothold, and in the dark I was stuck. There was nothing to do but wait for the clouds to leave the moon.

Squatting close to the wall, with jacket collar turned up and hands deep in my pockets, I shut my eyes. The day had been long and I was sleepy. But just as I felt a nice doze coming on, a rock started down somewhere nearby. Listening to its bouncing progress and the dead silence that followed, I ruled out the idea of going to sleep. Besides, I had a quaint habit of sleeping kitty-corner across a bed and this ledge was hardly four feet wide.

I did not feel any cozier when I realized that on the lip of the cliff above was a lot of snow that might take a notion to organize a coasting party. In that case, the place for me would be flat on my face on the ledge. Obviously, this was no time for a nap.

I yawned and pulled my head farther down into my collar. This spot I was in was certainly no credit to a Forest Service Lookout entrusted with the responsibility of keeping fit till the end of the season. It was even worse now that a Lookout was a war worker, and Bill Sethe would have a dickens of a time finding a replacement. By the very act of leaving the station at midnight without asking permission, I had been a bad, bad girl, a sober fact that I now realized too late. Worst of all was the grisly knowledge that if I should follow the flashlight and the rock, the boys would have to waste a lot of precious time picking up my pieces.

Staring into denser darkness as clouds thickened over the moon, I wondered what Elmer would have to say about this. Something very caustic no doubt. But I would never tell him of course. The whole thing was too shameful.

It would be a pity not to tell him some day, though, because he would make a fine story out of it. That is, if I ever got back on top. Shivering with cold and suspense, I realized that possibly I might not be so lucky or resourceful as the old man in one of Elmer's stories.

The old boy had gone hiking with some young folks, wandered away by himself, and wound up in the gorge of Coal Creek. Twenty-four hours later, when a searching party was beating the brush on the wrong side of Coal Creek Mountain, the old man came sauntering onto the highway, none the worse for a night in the open and very smug about his woodsmanship, which had led him down the creek to the road.

"But weren't you terribly afraid of wild animals down in that awful canyon?" asked the gushy female tourist who had given him a lift.

"Wild animals!" he snorted. "Hell, lady! They ain't no wild animals been born which could get down where I went."

At my vision of the testy old hero exploding into his oath, I tittered, then caught my breath. A pebble had tinkled down and struck the ledge beside me. Perhaps there was a cougar up there! The thought came before I could stop it because, unlike the old man, I was none too sure that wild animals could not get down where I was.

Fiddlesticks! I snapped at myself. Cougars are too particular about their meals to waste good ration points on a human. Besides, they run like heck when you yell. Carefully I cleared my throat to get it in good working order, and went back to Elmer.

On Sunday he and Jimmie had been discussing the matter of getting lost in the woods, and Elmer had said that it is just plain silly to get lost. You can always keep yourself oriented by some conspicuous feature of the landscape. Or, if traveling through thick timber, memorize the contours of the earth. Or leave a string of blazes, that is, if you have anything to cut them with or a petticoat to tear up as the clever pioneer kiddies did when carried off by redskins.

A gun's handy too, said Elmer, for the standard distress signal of three shots. You shoot three times, then wait, then do it again. Part of what Elmer calls your "hulls" you save till later, just in case there's no one around to hear you at first. Then if nobody comes and you have to "lie out" as the boys put it, you make yourself snug behind a log, and to quote the "Professor," "think warm thoughts and calm your spirit."

But there I sat, with no gun, nobody to hear it if I did have, no trees to blaze, no petticoat to tie on bushes. No bushes even, to say nothing of a log to snuggle up to. Of all Elmer's pointers, the only one that was any use to me was "think warm thoughts and calm your spirit."

Casting around for some warm thoughts I struck on the weather. This was summer, of course, August 11—no, the wee small hours of August 12. Dog days. Arctic sled dog days to be exact. Or to be perfectly frank, it was damn cold!

Tut, tut! I scolded myself. Elmer simply cannot stand to hear a lady swear. But this was no time to concentrate on being a lady, not with the situation stripped down to fundamentals. Here I was, just a lone female human, set down in a spot as primitive as they come. For thirty days I had been kidding myself that I was practically a pioneer, akin to the wonderful pioneer women of covered-wagon days. Whereas all the time I had been as safe up there in my little glass house as behind the desk in geometry class. Safer, in fact, because it was in geometry once that a certain rugged young individualist had cut loose with an apple core and made a bull's-eye on the back of the teacher's head.

But tonight Tatoosh had evidently decided to show me that wind, darkness and a mountain can still cut a human being down to pint size in a hurry.

The wind was growing colder too, and the stars fewer, as the clouds gobbled more and more of the sky. As the last of the Big Dipper's handle went and I was deprived of even that dear old friend, I got lonesomer and lonesomer. This was such an alien, spooky spot. No wonder the Indians used to believe in demons.

Why, perhaps there was a demon right down there in the black basin, licking his lips and waiting for me to fall in. Come to think of it, the little lake, by day so innocently pale blue-green around its sparkling ice cake, was probably the den of the demon, from which he emerged after dark to prowl among the rocks on the basin's floor seeking what he might devour. He was doubtless a very horrible demon too, like the one in the old Indian legend of the "thing" and the grandmother.

A long time ago, it seems, a certain old lady lived in a cedar hut or a mat lodge, somewhere out west here with her five sons and one granddaughter. One day the sons all went deer hunting, leaving the mother and child at home. As afternoon wore on, the little girl ran in and out to see if her father and uncles were coming back.

But they were unusually late that day and it was dusk before she saw a lone figure approaching. Squealing with joy, she ran to tell her grandmother. Go out and meet him, said the old lady, and find out what's keeping the rest of my boys. So the little girl went racing, but when she came close to the lone figure she saw it was not a man at all. As the old tale puts it, the figure was a "thing" with "only one arm, only one leg."

Screaming with fright, the little girl tore back to the hut, but before grandmother could barricade the door, the "thing" walked in. Run find your father and uncles, cried grandmother, as the "thing" began prowling around the room. But as soon as the little girl had darted out, the "thing" seized grandmother, broke open her head, ate her brains, stuffed a snake in her empty skull, and carried her off.

When the sons finally came home and got on the trail, they found that the "thing" had taken their mother deep into a cavern, from which they could hear her laughing madly, as the snake writhed in her skull. Shaking their own heads sadly, they went away and left the old lady to her fate.

Looking up at the clouds over the moon, I saw the shape of a face, a twisted face such as grandmother's must have been, as she screamed out her laughter. I shuddered, remembering how the story describes grandmother's laughter—"Ha, ha-ha! Ha, ha, ha! Ha, ha-ha! ha-ha!" It was time I got back to the "Professor."

I took my numb hands out of my pockets, slapped them together to restore the circulation, and remembered Betty's remark to Elmer on Sunday after he had told a story at the dinner table. A little piqued because she had been taken in, she said she would like to slap him. He smirked proudly because nothing ever delighted Elmer more than success with his tree-squeak yarn. He had got his chance to tell it when I said something about having oiled the hinges on the door.

"Great jumping jack salmon!" he exclaimed. "Why did you ever do a thing like that? There you were, all set for another pet. If you'd let the door alone, you'd soon had a little tree squeak coming in to nibble the hinges."

"What's a tree squeak?" asked Betty. "Some little animal?"

"Lives in trees," answered Elmer.

"What do they look like?" she inquired.

"Well, they're hard to get a look at," he told her. "But according to the best view I ever got of one, they're larger than a ground squirrel, smaller than a chipmunk, with a tail like a beaver and long sharp teeth like a cougar."

"Funny-looking things," she commented.

"Smart, though," said Elmer. "The old ones are said to chase the babies out of the nest and send them to the high country to cut their teeth on these little alpine firs. Come winter, they're grown up and ready to go down and feed on the big cedars and Douglas firs and hemlocks."

"But what part of the trees do they eat?" she quizzed. "I thought only woodpeckers ate trees."

"Well," countered Elmer, "naturally what part of a tree would a tree squeak eat?"

"But I can't imagine!" she wailed.

"Why, the squeaks, of course," answered Elmer.

That was when she threatened to slap him. At recollection of the look on her face, I laughed out loud, then stopped quickly as I remembered grandmother's wild "ha-ha's." The sound of my own mirth seemed weirdly out of place here where the wind, the murmuring waters of Stevens Creek over in the north, and the trickling pebbles from the cliff face spoke of things beyond the range of human laughter.

The wind, curving down over the edge of the ridge, was speaking with a gusty roar like the roar of the western sea from which it came. It roared of mysteries of the sea, perhaps of salmon hearing and heeding the call to return to the place of their birth, to spawn and die. I had seen them spawning and dying in Butter Creek, and marveled at the insistence of life on perpetuating itself.

Stevens Creek was speaking too, murmuring secrets of its creek bed, of the contours of its channel, of rocks under its foaming riffles, rocks belched up from the earth by fire or thrust up by some mighty folding of its crust. How many secrets Stevens Creek must know, I mused, secrets that man may never learn. Secrets, perhaps, of life and death.

Even the pebbles trickling from the cliff face spoke of the laws of life by which the earth itself must live, the laws that tell unstable things to fall, mountains to be humbled by wind and rain and frost. I had seen the record of these laws on the floor of the basin, in the long lines inscribed by falling rocks on the banks of snow curving from the basin's center up its walls. And if I were to fall like a rock from this ledge, I too would write one slender line in the basin's book and then lie still, a grotesque question mark at the end.

But I was not going to fall if I could help it. Like all other living things I was under some powerful urge to stay alive. I had seen that urge at work on Tatoosh, in the greed of Impie, the antic gleanings of the chipmunks, the protective brown and white of ptarmigan, the coupled dancing of two butterflies.

Here on Tatoosh there was no disguising the fact that the principal business of life is keeping alive. Deer, mosquitoes, white-footed mice, the little alpine firs, the flowers, all were doing their best to make it plain that those to whom the privilege of life has been given are duty-bound to struggle to live. Feeling my eyes closing, I strained them open, reminding myself of Impie's eternal vigilance, his courageous acceptance of the laws of life.

What a squirrel does I can do, I told myself. Then on second thought I doubted that. In Impie's behavior were aspects of daring, resourcefulness, strength and endurance not to be found in mine. Numb and impotent on my prison shelf, with freedom wide but un-attainable around me, I was a poor weak creature compared to Impie, snuggled safe in his burrow.

I did not amount to much compared to the coyotes, either. They were still on the prowl, flinging their jabbering mirth into the night, just like grandmother, "Ha, ha-ha! Ha, ha-ha!"

Abruptly I realized that if the coyotes kept that up much longer I would soon be laughing madly too. The weird amusement seemed to be everywhere, above, around and below me, even beside me on my narrow perch. In a moment of near-panic I stood up to throw off the horrid spell. Then, as I felt myself gripped by a wild desire to jump off the ledge, I sat down again.

If that moon would shine out for just one instant, I thought hysterically, I would be off this ledge like a rubber ball and over the top in one great bounce. But the moon stayed hidden, and I stayed put, while the coyotes kept on howling.

"Shut up!" I almost screamed the words. Then, surprised at the sound of my own voice, I tried it again, to be sure it was really mine and not that of some mocking demon.

"Shut up!" I shouted, flinging the foolish command toward the black northwest where the coyotes howled.

Strangely enough, they did shut up, as if for a moment the little yellow wolves were trying to figure out what I meant. Then, as if they had got my meaning and chosen to defy it, they burst into an answering howl that was the very voice of derision itself.

"Shut u-u-u-p!" I tried again, longer, louder, more frantically. Again the quiet, then the answer. It was a skin-pricking business, arguing with coyotes from a four-foot ledge above a void, in the middle of a freezing summer night. But it was better than nothing.

I had opened my mouth for another rebuttal, when the yell broke off in my throat. There had come a rattle close above me, a sharp impact just over my head, then the whiz of a good-sized rock as it sped down toward the basin. Glued to the wall, I stared up. What had loosened that rock? The vibration of my shouts? A cougar? A bear? A brush ape?

Suddenly I could not stand it any longer, though reason was trying to tell me that the rock had simply come loose and tumbled of its own accord. Terror was yelling, "Climb, climb!"

Without stopping to remember that the mere idea of climbing in this thick dark was ridiculous, I began to paw the cliff face with my hands. It was smooth; I had seen that it was smooth in the light of the torch. Still—.

"What's that?" A tiny crack about the height of my knee above the ledge, a toehold? Even though I could not believe it, I shoved in the toe of one tennis shoe, braced myself, then lifted my weight off my other foot. My toe stayed put for a second, proving that the crack had possibilities if I could find a handhold.

Eagerly I pawed again and found a tiny jagged spot on which the finger-tips of my left hand got a tentative grip. A moment later I was clinging to the face of the cliff like a wet leaf, holding my breath, at least eighteen inches above the prison of the ledge.

In daylight I might have thought nothing of it. But in the dark, with the wind jostling me first from one side, then from the other, I had almost no sense of balance. Then my other toe, gingerly exploring, found a small bump. Now able to reach a little farther to the right, I caressed the wall with my right hand till my fingers curved like claws into a fair handhold. I got a good grip and decided to give myself one of Elmer's "fives."

Suddenly the whimsical face of Elmer himself appeared in the deep gray of the rock close to my eyes. He seemed to be saying something. "Why don't you pray, schoolma'am? Why don't you pray?"

Good idea, I thought, and prayed. "God," I said right out loud, "I got myself into this, but You'll have to get me out."

It was not much of a prayer, but it made me feel better. Taking my right foot off its bump and using it to scrape the rock, I discovered what felt like a tiny ledge. Now if I could contrive to move my whole body in that direction I might reach brand-new territory and locate holds by the dozen.

With fingers biting into the rock, I shifted my center of gravity slowly, slowly, with only the straining of muscles to tell me what silly position I was in. If Elmer's face had moved around in back of me, it must have been grinning.

The little ledge was barely large enough for both feet, but it felt like the top of a dining table. Then I found some sizable cracks for my fingers and was about to take another rest, when the coyotes cut loose again. Their jarring laughter almost threw me off my perch, and hastily I renewed my explorations. Then, suddenly—could this be a huge luxurious crack?

So startled that I nearly lost my balance, I pawed at the spot. It was not a crack but a shelf—a lovely, lovely shelf! A moment later I was on it, aware of something familiar about its contour. Then the glorious truth broke around me like a flood of moonlight. I had reached the shelf from which I had slid to the ledge. And above were holds and holds and holds, clear to the top of the cliff!

Testing each hold, I climbed slowly but steadily. The night lost its last shreds of gray as the clouds took over the whole sky. Blackness brushed my cheeks, caught at my hair, clogged my nostrils. I felt stifled. Weak and confused, I misjudged a foothold. For a short but awful moment I wondered how it was going to feel to hit the bottom of the basin. When I lit on my feet a little way down, I decided to say my prayers again and ask for sense enough to keep my mind on what I was doing.

When at last I went sprawling over the rim of snow at the top of the cliff, all I could do was lie there shaking and muttering, "Thanks, thanks, a million times thanks!"

Then, with my face in a frosty plant at the edge of the snow, I stiffened and lay still. The diary! Where, on God's earth, was the diary? Not in my hands, not in my pockets, not under my arm! I had climbed up and left the diary down there on that dreadful ledge!

For agonizing seconds I wondered what to do. Go up to the house, get another flashlight, climb back down to that ledge? No, no, I could never do it! But I would have to. There was no getting away from it. That was what I had to do.

Groaning, I rolled over. And as I rolled, something flopped against my ribs. The diary, the blessed, blessed diary, safe inside my shirt!

Flat on my back on the snow, I laughed till I could not laugh any longer. Laughed wildly, like grandmother, "Ha, ha-ha! Ha, ha-ha!" But it was glorious laughter. And when at last I stopped and lurched to my feet, as groggy as a funny man in the movies, the coyotes took up the goofy theme and carried on.

"Ha, ha-ha! Ha, ha-ha!" they screamed. The most wonderful sound I had ever heard.

Henry David Thoreau, Fire Lookout

DON SCHEESE

FOR THE PAST nine summers I have worked as a fire lookout for the U.S. Forest Service in Idaho. When not gazing at cloud formations and scanning the forest for fires, I've devoted my time to reading all of Thoreau's work, and have become fascinated with the question of how his life might have changed had he been able to man a fire tower.

It's a moot question, of course. The first official fire lookout, Bertha Hill, did not exist until 1902. But the possibility is intriguing. Lawrence Buell has observed that "it was a favorite Transcendental pastime to brood over one's vocation," and Thoreau brooded over his as much as any Transcendentalist. When his books failed to sell he turned eventually to surveying to generate income and also to keep him out-of-doors, only to find the occupation dissipating. By surveying future homesites and property boundaries he was, after all, contributing to the disappearance of Concord's wildness. If only he could have been paid to study the local ecology and landscape aesthetics! Having read Thoreau's *Journal,* I'm convinced he would have been quite happy as a lookout and made an excellent firewatcher. He had the appropriate temperament; he loved the mountains and solitude; and he was a "pyromantic."

The late Edward Abbey, a nature writer often compared to Thoreau and a former lookout himself, once wrote that "the technical aspects of a lookout's job can be mastered by any literate anthropoid with an IQ of not less than seventy in about two hours. It's an attitude that's difficult: Unless you have an indolent, melancholy nature, as I do, you will not be happy as an official U.S. government fire lookout."

This is no exaggeration. If one can read a map and the surrounding terrain, and learn how to use a compass-like device called the Osborne Firefinder, the basic qualifications have been met. Most important is temperament; a lookout is required to scan the horizons with binoculars every twenty minutes from nine A.M. to six P.M. each day. Sounds easy, but it's not. One person's reaction to the occupation is typical: "I'd go nuts in a job like that!" But Thoreau intimated he might have been happy as a lookout when prior to moving to Walden Pond, he wrote in his journal: "But my friends ask what I will do when I get there. Will it not be enough to watch the progress of the seasons?"

"How to make the getting of our living poetic!" was a question Thoreau often contemplated. He would have had a ready answer had he lived atop a mountain. Fire lookouts by design are situated on the highest peaks in a region in order that visibility be maximized. For someone who claimed "it is worth the while to see the mountains in the horizon once a day," Thoreau's ecstasy while living in a twelve by twelve foot mountain cabin is not hard to imagine. (Incidentally, the dimensions of his home at Walden were twelve by fifteen feet.) He often walked to the cliffs near Fair Haven Hill to enjoy the view and sunsets. In June 1854 he went there "to see the sun go down, to recover sanity and put myself again in relation with Nature." A mountain home, he once punned, would be *real* estate. On another occasion he considered "the value of the mountains in the horizon . . . a good theme for a lecture . . . a sermon on the mount."

One of the standard tools of a lookout is a cloud chart describing in photos and words the successive stages of a thunderstorm, from towering cumulous to lightning. Thoreau was a connoisseur of clouds. In his journal for 24 April 1857 he sketched stages 4 and 5 clouds representing virga and rainfall.

Thoreau often climbed the mountains of New England for the views and the solitude high country offers. His near-ascent of Mt. Ktahdin in 1846 is famous, but less well-known is the fact he climbed Mt. Washington in New Hampshire twice and lesser peaks of the region many other times. After climbing in the White Mountains on one occasion, he drew a profile of the peaks to help him memorize the terrain. Today lookouts use panoramic photographs of the surrounding country for the same purpose.

Finally, Thoreau was a "pyromantic"—an essential qualification for anyone associated with firefighting. His nonchalant behavior following the fire he set in the woods near Concord—climbing the cliffs to observe its progress—earned him the opprobrium of numerous towns-men. Lightning-struck trees were "sacred spots," and lightning storms "the artillery of the heavens" and "the forked thunderbolt of the poets." Like any good lookout Thoreau craved the sight of wildfires; he fre-quently reported them in his journal and once, from the cliffs, spotted five separate fires burning simultaneously.

Thoreau so often climbed Fair Haven Cliffs that it can be said the site *was* his lookout. On 29 May 1857 he started his ascent, only to have it rain halfway up. So he sought shelter under an overhanging rock. Suddenly lightning struck close by, and Thoreau experienced the com-bination of fear and exhilaration unique to firewatching. "Who knows but the lightning will strike this cliff?" he wondered. But gradually the storm passed and Thoreau, always the philosopher, pondered the sig-nificance of the event. He realized how, once he sought shelter, he looked at the scenery in a new way. "This Cliff became my house. I inhabited it." So comfortable did he become that he even sang "Tom Bowling," his favorite song, while the storm raged!

For several hours, then, Thoreau *was* a fire lookout, an inhabitor of the mountains. Had lookouts been in existence in his time, he could have been an inspector, not of snowstorms, but *thunder*-storms. His life-long quest for the suitable vocation would have been satisfied, and per-haps he might have written yet another *Walden*-like book—casting stones at civilization from his glass house in the clouds.

Saying Good-bye to Bell Mountain Summers

BRADLEY BLUM

ASK ANYONE WHO'S been a fire lookout for any length of time. I think most will tell you it's job they won't easily give up.

It's a need for both what often comes with the job and what doesn't. On the tangible side, several things come readily to mind.

First, there are the panoramic views. From my lookout on Bell Mountain, I can see most of southern Idaho on a clear day. Just to the north loom the Pioneer Mountains, the most impressive aspect of my surroundings, with several peaks in the neighborhhod of twelve thousand feet. Even in years when the snowpack has been light, some of these south-facing slopes still hold snow through most of July.

Then there's the wildlife. Blue grouse regularly stroll up to the lookout to pick up a little gravel for their crops or to snip off dandelion greens. Elk and mule deer can occasionally be seen moving to and from the brush patches on the mountain's south face. And during my first summer, a young buck with forked antlers would boldly cross the peak just yards from the lookout on his way to a snowbank, where he would lie down and roll to get relief from the flies. And too, I've encountered a couple bears over the years, and there's hardly a time when I can't see a hawk, eagle, or buzzard soaring on the updrafts somewhere nearby. Furthermore, I know there are mountain lions in the area, but I've yet to have the good fortune to spot one.

The sunsets far surpass anything seen by the unfortunate commoner trapped down in the valley. What might seem a run-of-the-mill end to the day to someone down in Hailey surrounded by twenty-five-hundred-foot-high valley walls is an entirely different experience for those atop Bell Mountain who can see a thunderhead shifting into red, pink, and orange off on the eastern horizon forty miles away. And speaking of thunderclouds, watching thunderstorms from a lookout can be exhilarating or frightening, depending on whether you're faint of heart and your building is well grounded or not. For me, the chance to see some of the storms I've watched was reason enough to take this job.

Just as important as what you get with the fire lookout is what you don't get: the daily commute to work, a desk with a view of the parking lot (if you have a window at all), a constantly ringing telephone, deadlines, and personality conflicts with the boss and coworkers. You, of course, may add or substitute your own workplace grievances.

A lookout's job, at least judging from my experience, comes without hassles. The only real expectations are that you be there when you're supposed to be, take accurate weather readings, communicate reasonably well on the radio, perform a little upkeep, treat visitors courteously, and of course, spot the smokes in timely fashion. It's not exactly a pressure cooker up there.

That said, I have to admit I have a little problem. I was born and raised in the Midwest in a Lutheran family. I thought I'd managed to overcome that handicap, but it seems a bit of the Protestant work ethic must have stuck with me. For four or five months of the year, I have a job I enjoy that places no noticeable stress on my body or mind. And there are times I feel the good old Protestant guilt for getting paid for this job. I must be committing a sin to have it so good.

Furthermore, after finishing my first Bell Mountain summer in 1989, I took a job that I've held in the off-seasons since. Though working as a counselor at the local state employment office isn't a bad job, it's bad enough that I keep promising myself I won't go back for yet another seven- or eight-month stint. Nevertheless, it is a job where I'm needed only from October or November until June, when I return to Bell Mountain. The money's not bad, and the insurance that comes with it is a big plus. Other winter jobs in the Sun Valley area are either sporadic or pay little better than minimum wage.

So, the combination of guilt about my Bell Mountain summers and the unavailability of a winter job equal to or better than what I've got frequently causes me to seek a regular, year-round job, and regrettably, a return to "normal" life. Such a transition would be far more palatable if it came in the fall at the end of a fire season, but it never seems to work out that way. My efforts to line something up as the end of summer nears have always failed, with the exception of that first year. But come spring, after a winter of office confinement and dealing with the unemployed public, when my memories of Bell Mountain and the anticipation of another summer there are what keep my thumbs from ending up on someone's trachea, that is when job offers practically fall from the sky into my lap.

This past spring, 1993, it was a pair of job offers from newspapers, one a small daily in Nevada, the other a small weekly in Alaska. I declined the first after reviewing a sampling of the paper that revealed the owners to be stationed way out on the right fringe of the political-philosophical spectrum. The other was tougher to say no to, since I've always wanted to go to Alaska and the owners seemed like folks I could get along with. But I didn't think the salary was enough for Alaska's high cost of living, they didn't have group health insurance, and they wanted me up there on extremely short notice.

Those two offers illustrate the ease with which I can land a job in the spring, when I don't really want one.

But it was the spring before, 1992, when I came dangerously close to losing my summer in the lookout. In my position at Job Service, I'd written up a lot of job orders for a local electrical engineering company, one of our area's largest employers. I had even seen a couple of orders for technical writers come through and entertained the thought of applying myself. Instead, though, I'd called other local journalists, including a friend and former coworker who had my old job as an editor. A little more than a year after he landed that job, the company was growing at such a phenomenal pace that nobody there seemed to know exactly how large the work force was at any given time, and they had advertised for two more technical writers.

Again, I toyed with the idea of going after one of the positions, but I had reservations, especially since it was nearly the beginning of another fire season. Some of this company's endeavors, such as showing Eastern European countries how to reduce pollution from their electrical generating plants and improving the efficiency of American facilities, struck me as beneficial works. But in terms of the big picture, I had some philosophical problems with their engineering of new transmission lines and substations to facilitate this country's gluttonous appetite for electricity and their participation in dam projects on South American rivers. I also had an uneasy feeling about the rate at which the company was expanding. Experience teaches us that booms are usually followed by busts. Most of all, I doubted my own ability to thrive in a technical environment. After all, I dropped high school chemistry after only one quarter and never took more than the bare requirement of math courses in high school or college.

Over a few beers one Friday night, I talked with my friend, and to my surprise, he professed to enjoy the job. His description of it didn't exactly elevate my heart rate, but he assured me that I was well suited for the work and urged me to send in my resume. After all, he pointed out, with the money I would make, I could fatten up my savings account in a hurry and move on to something else in a couple of years, if I wanted. The two former editors from the area's other weekly paper both had told me they liked their jobs there, too. Well, I thought, if he likes it there at "the home for old editors," as he said the company's business development group had been nicknamed, maybe I'd like it too. Still, I didn't feel compelled to rush home and send out a resume.

At that time, I was newly involved in a romantic entanglement. I mentioned the job opening to her, said I was thinking about applying, and recounted my Friday night chat at the hotel's bar. Though I had reservations, she certainly didn't. It sounded like a wonderful opportunity to her. I'd make more money, which would give me more spending money when I ran away on the around-the-world trip she'd decided we were going to take. (She was picking up the tab for the tickets.) And if I worked in town, she'd get to see a lot more of me than she would if I was off on top of a mountain. Although she didn't say so, I'm also convinced that she thought it more respectable for a woman of her social position to have a boyfriend who worked for a consulting engineer, rather than one who spent his summers sitting on top of a mountain and his winters working as some kind of government bureaucrat. Given her enthusiasm, I agreed to apply for the job.

Again, I didn't feel compelled to run right to my word processor and get on the task. But after a couple evenings of her prodding, I finally sat down and wrote a cover letter telling the manager of the business development group why I wanted to work for her and why she should want to hire me. Although I didn't think the letter sounded all that convincing, my romantic interest thought it was quite good. I mailed it with a resume and would have forgotten about it, except that she kept asking if I'd heard anything back from the company.

About a week later, I did hear back from the manager, and we got together over lunch. Predictably, I was quizzed that evening about how it had gone, and for the next few evenings I was repeatedly asked if I'd heard anything from the company.

When I did hear, the manager called and asked me, with some

trepidation, if I would come to work for them for $11 an hour. I said yes, but not without experiencing a tightening sensation in my chest. She said she was glad to hear me say that, because she'd been turned down by the first two people she'd offered a job that day. Both had wanted more money. That really bolstered my confidence. It's always nice to know you're somebody's third choice. I shook off my uneasiness, though, and asked when she wanted me to start. Monday, June 1, I was told.

I was scheduled to report to the BLM's fire headquarters in Shoshone on June 8 that year, and I'd timed my departure from Job Service accordingly.

Later that day, however, I got a call from my romantic interest, who was in southern California to provide support for a friend who was having a facelift (and to get her own eyes worked on a bit, as long as she was there). She wanted to know if I'd heard anything about the job yet. When I told her that I'd just taken it and that I was to start in two weeks, she suggested that I give myself a week off and fly to California and spend some time with her. I could drive back with her and her friend and be home a day or two before I was to start the new job. I told her I'd see how my boss at Job Service, who was out of the office, would react to the idea of my leaving at the end of that week.

When the boss got back, I pitched the idea of my leaving on what amounted to four days' notice. Predictably, she didn't like it. Almost as predictably, I was able to whine enough about how this wasn't like my usual departure for an idyllic summer, but a real job, and I probably wouldn't get any vacation time for at least a year, that she grudgingly gave in—on the condition that my coworkers didn't object. They didn't. So when I got another call from California later that day, I was able to say I could come down. Good thing, too, because she'd already made my reservations.

I can't say that I did a lot of fretting about my career decision on the way to California, nor during my time there. But just before leaving I got a phone call from an old college friend who's kind of a sister to me. When I told her what I was about to do, she told me I had sold out. I agreed with her assessment but thought that put me in an awfully large club. I believed I had come to terms with my decision. Besides, I was having fun. I frolicked in the surf at Newport Beach, La Jolla, and Big Sur, ate seafood and drank champagne at beachfront restaurants almost every day, walked the streets of Monterey and Pacific Grove, and otherwise did a lot of things I would normally scoff at as "touristy."

It wasn't until my vacation was nearly over that I had my head-on collision with reality. The Saturday before I was to start my new job, we drove back into Idaho up U.S. 93, crossing the Snake River north of Twin Falls and climbing toward the mountains and the Wood River Valley. South of Shoshone we came in view of the Notch Butte lookout.

Notch Butte is a desolate outpost atop a dormant volcano on the Snake River Plain. Its view is primarily of vast sagebrush expanses and farmlands claimed from the desert. The lookout is less than a mile from the highway, and the person stationed there just puts in eight-hour days and doesn't stay overnight. It's a far cry from Bell Mountain. But the sight of Notch Butte lookout hit me like a hard jab in the belly because I associated it with the Bell Mountain lookout. My lookout. But my lookout no longer.

I made the rest of the trip to Hailey in gloomy silence. Any attempts by my two female traveling companions to engage me in conversation drew only grunts or, at best, one-word answers. When we arrived where I'd left my pickup in Hailey, I unloaded my suitcase, hugged one of my companions, kissed the other, and bade them good-bye.

I drove downtown, picked up my mail, and went to the liquor store, where I bought a six-pack of ale. Then I drove south, stopping off at my storage unit for a sleeping bag, fishing rod, and tackle box, and then dropped by a self-serve nightcrawler stand.

Normally, for me, fishing is an activity that is the culmination of a backpacking trip to a high mountain lake. If the fish aren't biting or the lake doesn't even have fish, the trip, the exercise, and a spectacular view are reward enough. But there are times when something in me yearns for the kind of fishing I knew in my late adolescence and early adulthood back when I lived in the Midwest. It's fishing that's mostly sitting and drinking beer, maybe getting stoned, if you've got the weed. Fishing with a worm, usually for the lowly bullhead catfish.

For the occasions when a mood for this kind of fishing hits me—be it nostalgia, laziness, or on this evening, melancholy—my favorite place is Carey Lake. It's not so much a lake as a marsh with narrow channels, low islands, and large expanses of reeds, cattails, and grass. Its fish species include bass, perch, and the bullheads for which I go there. In the spring and summer months, there's a constant din of quacking ducks, honking geese, and, well, whatever you would call the sounds sandhill cranes make.

When I arrived at Carey Lake that Saturday night, there was about an hour of daylight remaining. I sat down on the bank of the channel, cracked open an ale, rigged up hook, sinker, and bait, and cast into the middle of the channel. As it grew dark, I still hadn't had a bite, but the liquor store ale (considerably more potent than the stuff you get in the supermarket) was giving me a pretty good buzz. I left my line out for an undetermined time past dark, until the ale was gone, and still hadn't gotten a bite. Giving it up, I rolled out my sleeping bag, crawled in, and, given my anesthetized state, fell quickly asleep.

My trip to Carey Lake wasn't really a conscious attempt to find any great truths. I think I just wanted to go there because, in addition to its conduciveness to drinking beer, it was the time of the year when I typically went there to check out the fishing, and I wanted to go to sleep to the sounds of all those birds. So it came as something of a surprise to me when I experienced a vision.

Now a vision, as far as I can tell, isn't really all that mystical an experience. It's just something that rises out of your subconscious in response to a matter that's been drawing a lot of energy in your conscious realm. Frequently, the trigger mechanism is the consumption of one or more drugs. If the truth be known about most visions of a religious nature, they were either the result of something the prophet in question ate, or didn't eat, since prolonged fasting causes the body to produce its own hallucinogens. In my particular case that May night, when my liver finished processing the alcohol out of my blood a couple hours before dawn, I began to have a very vivid dream. (For me, any dream I remember the next morning is vivid.)

This dream that I deemed a "vision" had myself and several people whom I couldn't identify in a large expanse of asphalt. There was, however, one man I did recognize. He was one of the "chronic cases" at the Job Service office. He was chronically unemployed, chronically drunk, chronically unwilling to put much effort into finding a job, and chronically having problems with his employers when he did stumble onto something. Not much was said in this dream, and the only activity was this man, the other people, and me crawling about this parking lot with knives in our hands. With these knives, we were attempting to pry coins out of the asphalt.

I awoke from this dream as the sky in the east was beginning to show a faint glow. After thinking about it for a while, I fell back into a fitful sleep until the sun was fully up. When I emerged from my sleeping bag, I walked down the canal to where the inflow from a hot spring joins it and took up fishing again. I had a little more success, catching a good-sized bass, but it was still pretty slow, and I gave up the endeavor about 9 A.M. I needed to hike to clear my head of the brain cells killed by the ale and ponder the meaning of my vision.

For years, I'd looked through my telescope from Bell Mountain at the Little Wood River's upper canyon where it emerges from the south slope of the Pioneer Mountains, but I'd never been there. That Sunday morning, I decided to change that.

After parking at the gate where the BLM Wilderness Study Area begins and beyond which vehicles are prohibited, I followed a trail into the timbered river bottom. The river, I soon discovered, had undergone extensive damming by beavers, and most of the trail now lay underwater. Eventually I gave up wading upstream in the hope that it would reappear, and climbed up the western slope of the canyon to the ridgeline. I followed it for a while, then dropped over the other side and bushwhacked down a small gulch to eventually pick up the trail and return to my truck.

In the course of this short, but arduous journey, I considered my vision. Eventually, I decided that the presence of the man I saw so frequently on the unemployment line coupled with the fact that we were prying nickels and dimes out of the pavement must mean that it was time for me to quit scratching for small sums and start making some decent money. That apparently meant that my decision to take the job as a technical writer and the $11 an hour (which some might say is a paltry sum, but a substantial increase over my pay at Job Service, or the BLM, and especially better than any salary I'd ever gotten at a newspaper) was a good one. So I told myself.

The next morning, I drove to the complex where I was to work and went to the annex building, where I'd been told the business development group was housed. It was a one-story, steel-sided structure that could easily be a machine shed or hoghouse were it located on a farm. Every eight or ten feet, the flow of the sheets of steel siding was interrupted by narrow vertical windows. Inside, these slots provided little light, and the interior was coolly illuminated by fluorescent tubes and computer screens.

Once inside, I located the desk of the woman who hired me. She led me to the windowless cubicle I was to occupy, which hadn't been completely vacated by its previous occupant, one of my old editor friends who was being promoted to a job that would take him to the company's main building. That building, an imposing (at least for our little town) three-story concrete structure a short walk from the annex, was our next destination. The manager led me over there to a conference room where I was to receive my orientation, along with another half dozen people who were starting work that day, including a handsome young man in his early twenties who had also been hired as a technical writer.

Following this session on what the keys we were issued would open, how we were to code telephone calls according to job billing, the particulars of our health insurance benefits, and a host of other vital instructions, all of the new hires except the other technical writer and me dispersed. He and I were left there, in this room decorated with photographs of substations and power lines, while we waited to be led to the next step. In chatting with him, I learned that he'd worked that winter for Sun Valley Company and before that for a public radio station after graduating from college. He told me he hadn't liked being a reporter because he didn't like asking people questions they didn't want to answer, so this type of work seemed more suited to him.

As I pondered why I had always enjoyed the little game that was played when I asked public officials questions they didn't want to answer, we were taken to the cubicle of the person whose task was to bring us up to a functioning level on the company's computer. For the remainder of that day, I sat at the terminal in my cubicle going through the steps in a self-paced instruction manual and occasionally calling my trainer to update her on my progress. At five o'clock, I was told by the friend who had encouraged me to apply for the job (and, I learned, also had assured the manager that I really wasn't "too laid back" to fit in, which she had feared I might be) that I should get out of there, because after the first week, it would be a rare day when I could leave after only an eight-hour stint.

That evening, the romantic interest wanted to know how I liked the job so far. I told her the first day had been all right, but I couldn't generate much enthusiasm about it or the prospect of going back the next morning.

I did go back the next morning. And, after getting my cup of coffee, resumed learning how to operate the computer. At about ten forty-five, the manager and I and the other new writer were scheduled to meet for a conference. After some idle chitchat about how things were going for us, the manager launched into what I think is the standard speech for new hires about the company's philosophy. She said that the company had started off with two rules: Do the best job you possibly can, and have fun. She said that later they had found it necessary to add a third rule: Make money.

That said, she hauled out some examples of what the business development group did. The thick, bound volumes she laid on the table were proposals to various utilities to hire our company to provide consulting engineering for their projects. She picked out one of the smaller ones, a proposal for rebuilding an aging electrical transmission line, and proceeded to show us what such a document consisted of. By the time this meeting concluded at noon, I was so bored that the only thing keeping me awake was the feeling of dread that was threatening to squeeze a sob from my chest. I couldn't imagine how I was going to have fun doing this, which was going to make doing a good job diffi-cult, leaving me with only one of the three rules—make money.

I drove to a downtown deli on my lunch break and sat at one of the picnic tables outside, trying to take solace in the fact that I was outdoors and it was a hot, sunny day. I noticed that the heat was producing some towering cumulus clouds and that they appeared to be massing in the south for an attack on the valley.

Later, as I pulled into the company's parking lot, I heard the first low rumbles of thunder emanating from the storm.

Fifteen minutes or so later, we heard the sharp cracks of thunder reporting nearby lightning. Several people went to the south door to watch. Seeing others out there, I decided I wouldn't get in trouble if I had a look. After all, we were in the electricity business. As something of an expert on electrical storms, I can say the one we witnessed from that doorway was a good one. (Or a bad one, depending on your per-spective.) Downstrikes were hitting the hills to the southwest of Belle-vue at the rate of one every minute or less.

As others began returning to their desks, I decided to go back to my cubicle, both because I was a new guy and didn't want to be seen malingering and because watching this spectacle was making me miser-able by reminding me of what I wouldn't be doing that summer. But when somebody came in and reported smoke rising from the hills to the southwest, I was back at the door in an instant.

The fire appeared to be a couple miles south of Bellevue, where the valley opens up and spills out into the flatlands. Someone at the door commented that it seemed to be in the vicinity of a ranch owned by the company's CEO and founder. This time, when I returned to my desk, it was strictly because the sight outdoors was making me utterly miserable. It was all I could do to keep myself from crying about what I'd done to the coming summer with this decision of mine.

After what must have been about a half hour of stewing in this state and making no progress on the task of learning the computer, I came to a decision. I rose from my desk and walked down the aisle past the group's staff assistant and out the door to the parking lot. I got in my pickup, fired it up, backed out of the space, and drove out of the parking lot and toward the highway. I turned south toward Bellevue, which was the nearest place I could think of where I could find a pay phone. At the phone booth, I punched in the number, which was a long distance call, and deposited the necessary coins.

"Hello. Fire Management," came the voice of a man I couldn't identify on the other end.

"Hi. This is Brad Blum. Andy Payne's the new FMO this year, right?" I asked, though I knew he was.

"Right. You want to talk to him?"

"Yes, please."

I'm not a religious person, but in the interval while I waited for Andy to come to the phone, I gave praying my best effort.

"Hello, Brad. What's up?" Andy asked abruptly, sounding like a man in the middle of being in charge of a fire-fighting effort.

"Did you fill my job yet? I mean do you have someone hired for the Bell Mountain lookout?" I held my breath.

"Well, we offered it to somebody . . ." I let out my breath and closed my eyes as he said this. ". . . but she declined it, and we haven't gotten around to offering it to this other guy we have in mind. Why?"

"This new job was a mistake, Andy. Unless I've screwed myself out of my rehire rights by resigning, I'd like to go back to the lookout this year."

"No problem. If you want to come back, you can."

"I can't thank you enough. I'll see you Monday morning."

As for my so-called vision, I don't know why that guy was in it. But I have since revised my interpretation to place more emphasis on the asphalt and less on the ne'er-do-well who was groveling for coins with me there. And what my subconscious was really trying to tell me was that the pursuit of money in a paved-over world is no substitute for a summer on Bell Mountain.

Adventure on High Rock Lookout

Bud Panco

THE FALL OF 1991 was warm and dry, and forest fires burned in several western states. A warm east wind had been blowing for several days, and the woods were tinder dry.

I was stationed on the High Rock Lookout, which, at 5,687 feet, is the highest point in the Sawtooth Range of the Cascade Mountains. It presents a commanding view of the Nisqually Valley and of Mount Rainier thirteen miles to the northeast.

High Rock is a good name for the lookout, because it sits on top of a huge rock fin with a 780-foot drop-off on one side and a 1,500-foot drop-off on the other—not the kind of place for those with a fear of heights.

The day broke clear and warm that October 13. Since it was a Sunday, I looked forward to quite a few visitors. The trail is only about one and a half miles long and allows both young and old to visit the oldest and one of the only three lookouts left in the Gifford Pinchot National Forest.

I rose at six thirty, made a check look from the catwalk with my 7×50 glasses, then made breakfast, washed the dishes, and took the weather at seven. I radioed the Packwood District dispatch, and it was decided that I could probably come down near the end of the week. The warm weather was predicted to break with wet storms, bringing an end to the fire season. At least that's what we hoped—it was the forty-third day with no rain, and seven days past when we usually closed the lookout. We needed rain bad.

October 14 started out warm, and again the east wind was blowing. I got my chores out of the way and was ready to spend some time chatting with visitors. I didn't expect the numbers I'd had on Sunday. But the fall colors were exceptionally bright because of the long, dry summer, and twenty-eight people came to the lookout that day, including two from Hawaii and one from Canada. The sunset was beautiful, with a long afterglow of yellows to a lingering deep red caused by dust in the upper atmosphere from the recent Philippine volcano eruption.

Tuesday, October 15, was another warm one. The east wind still blew. Not a cloud in the sky. Where was the rain?

The day ended with only three visitors. One, from England, came late in the afternoon and was taken by all the mountains. She was the last to come up, and when she left I was alone once again.

After supper, I sat and read until the sun went down.

I made a pot of coffee for morning, then went out on the catwalk to watch the moon and listen to the night. The warm east wind was still blowing, and I could hear the hooting of several owls and the sound of the Nisqually River drifting up from far below. I sat there until way after nine, before I went to bed, and there wasn't a cloud anywhere, just a big, beautiful moon in a dark blue sky.

Along about one thirty, I woke up to a strong wind coming out of the southwest. I raised up on my elbow and looked out the window. The moon was shining low on the western skyline. The lights of south Olympia shone in the distance. And still no clouds anywhere. "Boy, those weathermen are nuts. It's going to be nice again tomorrow." I rolled over and went back to sleep.

Sometime around three thirty, I woke with a start. The wind was screaming through the guylines and visibility was zero. The sound was like a jet engine. It would die down, and then I could hear it building up. Then it would come roaring in and hit the building like an express train. And there was no letup to either its sound or its fury.

The lookout shook and the shutters banged up and down. I couldn't sleep with all the noise and shaking. I got up, lit two candles, and warmed up the coffee.

I had just taken a sip and set the cup down and was standing with my back to the southwest corner when I heard this roar, like a low-flying jet, coming at me. "Man, I hope he's flying high enough to miss the lookout." Then there was a ripping sound of wood, and a bang that sounded like an explosion. The building was thrown up against the guylines. Coffee flew all over the place and the candles went out. Darkness.

For an instant, I thought a plane really had hit the building. I took a small flashlight out of my pocket. The first place I looked was up, to check the roof, then I checked the windows. The shutter on the southwest corner was gone, just gone.

I lit the candles again and moved them over to the cabinet along the north wall. The wind was still screaming, and the building still shook with every blast. I knew I was reasonably safe inside, but I wanted to check the damage.

Slipping on my jacket, I carefully opened the door and stepped out. The wind along the east side was strong, but when I stepped around the corner on the south side, it backed me up against the guyline and handrailing. I had to lean into the wind just to stand up, and I hung on to that handrail for dear life.

Battling the wind, I managed to shine the flashlight along the side of the building. I could see the shutter lying on the roof. A lookout shutter isn't some little aluminum decoration like you see in the city. It's a good, solid piece of three-quarter-inch plywood and must weigh 150 pounds. The wind had taken that shutter and split the facing board full length and bent the nails up like horseshoes.

I didn't realize that I had gotten wet until I was back inside. The rain had come.

Packwood dispatch doesn't come on the air until seven, so I cleaned up the coffee and heated some more and tried not to think about the 1,500 feet of blackness on one side of me and the 780 feet on the other. The storm continued screaming and raging while I waited for daylight and seven o'clock.

Never before had I experienced a wind like this, and though I wasn't eager to go outside, my curiosity was rising. So I went back out with the hand-held wind gauge that's standard issue for those on fire watch. Putting my finger over the top of the tube in order to lower the scale, I turned it into the wind. The little ball went instantly to the top and stuck there at sixty miles per hour. I knew it was way more than that.

That night was one of my longest, and I've lived a long time. I didn't feel any sadness at all as I packed my gear and waited for daylight. It was time to get out.

When I finally reached dispatch that morning, the answer that came back sounded like a mule braying. Their transmitter was having terrible feedback. I couldn't understand a word. Fortunately they could hear me and got on a different radio.

"Can you hear me now?" the dispatcher said.

"Affirmative," I replied, relieved by the sound of his voice, though with the wind roaring in the guylines, I could just barely hear him. "Can you hear the wind? I have a sixty-mile-plus up here. It blew the southwest shutter off, and it's lying up on the roof."

"If we send some guys up to help, can we get the other shutters down before we lose them?"

"No! The wind's too strong. We'd lose them all."

"Well, we were going to bring you down today anyway," he said.

I told him I'd finish packing up and radio when I was ready for someone to meet me at the trailhead. He signed off then, warning me not to do anything foolish.

There wasn't much left to do. I had one more trip to make outside to shut off the propane to the stove. The tanks were down under the building in a small storage room. Hanging on to the edge of the cat-walk, I went down and opened the door. It flew open with such force that it almost came off the hinges. I checked all around under the building with my flashlight. Everything looked good. I turned off the gas and made my way back up.

I was ready to leave. I'd checked everything twice. Now all I had to do was call Packwood. It was about seven thirty when I radioed and said I was going to start down, and that I would call again when I reached the shelter fifty yards down the mountain.

I waited on the lee side of the lookout, out of the wind, until I thought it had died down enough to start for the shelter. The last thing dispatch had said was "Good luck," and I needed it now. The wind finally paused and I started down. I'd gotten only a few yards from the building when I heard the roar of the wind building up for another blast. The rocks were slick from the rain, and there was nowhere to go if I slipped—nowhere but over the edge. I knew I was in trouble.

The best thing I could do, with my pack on, was to lie flat on the rocks and hold on. I was glad for the pack's extra weight. When the wind hit, it rolled me over onto my side against my pack. I don't know how long I was pinned there, and I don't remember being cold and wet. But I do remember wondering what a fall of fifteen hundred feet would feel like. A sky dive followed by instant death? A blackout before hitting bottom?

Then the wind seemed to die down, and I raised my head. I got on all fours, moving sideways like a crab, and made it down to the shelter.

Now all hell broke loose up at the lookout. I could hear the wind really screaming up above. I was glad to be down in the timber. From inside the shelter, I could hear trees falling, limbs breaking. Brown stuff flew through the air—Noble fir cones breaking up and the pieces windborne. I called Packwood and said I'd made it down to the shelter and that as soon as I caught my breath, I'd be starting down.

Now all I had to do was watch out for falling trees and limbs. I walked as fast as I could to keep warm. I reached the one-mile marker in a hurry and was down below the main force of the wind. From there I came across the first and only tree across the trail, about a quarter mile from the road.

Once down, I called Packwood and said I'd reached the road and was waiting for my ride.

"Your ride left at seven forty-five and should be there shortly." Then he asked me how the weather was up there.

"Hardly any rain or wind at the trailhead at this time," I said. I sat down on a rock to wait. Then the storm blew down on me.

The rain came down in buckets and the wind blew it with such force that it was like being peppered with icicles. I tried to get out of the way by going behind a cutbank on the turn in the road, but it came right down over the top. I tried the bank on the other side of the road. It helped some. Soaking wet and sitting down, I began to get cold. Time passed and still no ride. So I radioed to find out where it was.

"We're at Berry Creek," came the voice of Glen Howland. "Which road do we take, Bud?"

"Take the 8440, the next road to your left," I replied.

And I waited and waited. They'd gotten turned around somehow and missed the turnoff. They called me for directions.

Now things were getting kind of bad. I was getting colder and starting to shiver, and they were going in the wrong direction. Dispatch finally got them straightened out and headed the right way after they'd gone a few extra miles out of their way on that mountain road.

In the meantime, I started walking down the road to get warmed up. Walking down the 8440, I was about a hundred yards from the 84 road when I heard Glen say he'd passed the 8460 at the top of the hill. I knew it wouldn't be long now.

I was standing in the middle of the 84 road, having walked two and a half miles from the trailhead, when they found me. The pickup was nice and warm, and boy did it feel good.

When we arrived at the station, everyone had heard about the storm and what had happened. And those down in the valley with scanners got in on the story too. They teased me some about being scared and not going back up next summer.

Well, to tell the truth, I wasn't all that scared in the lookout, but out on the rocks, lying there spread-eagle, trying to hold on . . .

Did I go back up? Oh, yes. You might say I have a strong feeling for the place. It's called love.

The White Pickup

Jackie Johnson Maughan

I WORK A FIRE LOOKOUT on the Nez Perce National Forest in Idaho. Last year was my first season. My lookout is called Coolwater and is located on the big east-west ridge between the Lochsa and Selway River drainages. I'm two miles from the Selway-Bitterroot Wilderness to the east and due south is the Frank Church—all told, 4.2 million acres, the largest expanse of wilderness in the lower forty-eight states.

To my north is the Clearwater National Forest. I call it the Clear-cut because that's basically what I'm looking at—clear-cuts. The closest towns are Kooskia and Kamiah, population circa one thousand.

The reason I'm telling you this is that I want you to understand why, although my lookout's on a road, I wasn't expecting the number of visitors I got. There were 103 in August alone.

My first week or so I was glad for visitors because I was lonely and disoriented. It was nice to have that reassurance that if I wanted down, I could get down, pronto. I'd had to leave my car down at the ranger station because it couldn't navigate the road.

At any rate, there's a certain pattern that emerges when you observe something long enough. For example, the bluebirds and finches appear early mornings and evenings, the hummingbirds at midmorning. A pair of kestrels (sparrow hawks) make their rounds in the early morning, at noon, and again about six in the evening. A pair of rough-legged hawks usually visit at noon and late afternoon. I also see an occasional eagle, and I've twice seen a pair of goshawks. The eagles like stiff winds, and I've only seen the goshawks right in front of storms (the dark lip of the storm approaches, goshawks on its breath). And, like the birds, the human beings have their patterns.

First off, they come in either four-wheel drives or on dirt bikes.

I see them long before they reach me as they snake along the ridge road after it emerges from the trees. Usually I see their dust or, in the case of the bikes, hear the high-pitched whine of their engines.

Once they're within half a mile of the lookout, they disappear under a cutbank, a place carved by the road that is constantly eroding and full of rocks and boulders. This is where they really have to slow down and I know it will take them at least fifteen minutes to get to the lookout. This lag gives me time to put on a shirt, straighten up the maps, run a comb through my hair. Usually they don't come early in the morning, for which I'm grateful. If they do show up before eight, I simply don't let them up on the lookout. I keep the trapdoor latched from above. I mean, I may be up at six, but those two hours are mine. I'm not officially at work until I check in at eight.

But usually they start showing up about noon. They park down near the outhouse, and there's always a pause while everyone hits the head and I can hear the door swinging open and closed. (By the way, there's a really fine view of Fire Lake as you sit there—that is, if you leave the door open.)

Then I hear their voices, and their breathing if they're out of shape, as they climb the last hundred feet. As I said, the first and biggest wave usually peaks about two in the afternoon, then there's another about four, and then another about seven. This last group has it timed to make it back down the mountain before dark.

Now in addition to time of day, there are days of the week. Thursday through Saturday are the biggest, with the density reaching the top of the curve on Saturday. It drops off a bit on Sunday, and Monday is the day I can just about count on no visitors, especially in the morning.

I don't want to sound like I'm talking about hundreds of people here, just groups of two or three or once in a while as many as eight. But when you live in a place like mine, two or three people feels like a crowd—climbing up and down the stairs, tromping around on the catwalk, peering in at your stuff, borrowing your binoculars, asking questions that are perfectly logical, but start sounding dumb after you've heard them all summer.

Maybe I shouldn't complain so much about visitors; after all, that's part of my job, especially if someone's hurt. If that's the case, I'm here for them twenty-four hours a day.

I'm telling you all this so you'll have a feel for the very public yet very isolated nature of this work. You are, indeed, alone most of the time, especially in the psychological sense of having the intense responsibility of reporting fires rapidly and accurately, with emphasis on accurately. This country is steep and brushy, and most of it is unroaded. So foot travel is generally required to get to fires. If you're off by half a mile on your smoke report, you can cause the field crews a lot of grief.

Well, Monday—Monday morning in particular—is the day I save to do my laundry and get cleaned up. There's a spring two hundred feet down the mountain. Here I've placed a washbasin filled with water and put this inside a black plastic trash bag and set it so it's in the sun. That way I have warm water. At first I packed the water up to the lookout. This is not easy—hauling fifty pounds of water in a QVC container up a mountain while it sloshes back and forth on this kind of Trapper John pack frame they give you. No, I found out it was easier to take my underwear and socks and whatnot down to the water rather than vice versa.

So this is my system. The socks and underwear get the first treatment since they're the dirtiest. These I soak in the warm water. Next come the T-shirts and tanktops and running shorts. I don't even try to wash my jeans; they just have to stay dirty till I stuff what I can into a daypack and hike the six miles and fifty-four hundred feet down the mountain to the ranger station where I can pick up my car and drive into town to the laundromat. After everything's been through the wash cycle, I quick soap up my hair with the gray water, then dump the water so it courses down the road and not into the path of the spring. Then I refill the basin. And let me tell you, that water's cold. Anyway, I rinse out my hair, then swab off my body in sections, and finish up with the clothes. It takes four or five basins full to get all the soap out.

This is an important ritual for me. By the time Monday rolls around, I'm dirty and my clothes are dirty. The hardest thing about being a lookout is the scarcity of water and how hard it is to keep clean. At least, that's my view of it. This whole process takes about forty-five minutes. I'd enjoy it more if I had a clear view of the road. As it is, I can't see more than fifty feet in either direction and the spring is pretty noisy and I'm a little nervous about someone driving up on me while I've got my hair full of soap and my shirt off.

So now I hope you'll understand how irritated I was one Monday morning when I took my binoculars and glassed the road before going down to the spring and saw some jerk in a white pickup coming up the road. I watched as he crept along, cursing to myself because he was ruining my day.

I was expecting my husband, who was driving six hundred miles from the other end of the state. I hadn't seen him all summer and this was August.

My husband drives a blue truck. When I saw the dust down there, my heart took a leap, but I could see even without the binoculars that this truck was white. I'd been watching for days for that blue truck. A green truck would have been okay too because that'd be Forest Service and they might be bringing my mail and news from down below, and we could talk about important matters such as the merits of Whites versus Red Wing boots, or why propane tanks thread backward, or how to refold a forest map without making lumps in it.

Well, hell, there he was, coming at me as relentlessly as a swarm of horseflies, and I supposed I'd just have to go down and do my laundry after he left. After that I'd have to settle for a spit bath up in the lookout, because I didn't want to risk someone coming up on me later in the day. I was not happy and was frankly skeptical that I could be very nice or accommodating naming mountains and such for whoever it was in that truck.

As the truck came closer, my irritation grew. I wanted so much to see someone of my own, not another stranger. When the truck went under the cutbank, I decided I'd just put the chain on the trapdoor and make it look like I wasn't there. I'd have to keep low so they couldn't see me inside. Then I'd wait it out while they rattled around down there taking pictures or whatever.

Well, that's what I did. I could see before he went out of sight that it was a single driver, probably a man. He couldn't see me at this point unless he had binoculars. Even if he did, he'd be too worried about the road to think of looking up. I got some satisfaction thinking about that.

Like I said, I had the place all chained up and was crouched there on the floor. I heard him pull up down below. Then quiet after he shut off his engine. Then I heard the kind of noise hiking boots make on rocks. Whoever it was was moving fast and not panting at all. Then I heard someone call out, but I couldn't quite make out the words because the wind came up and the flag started flapping. Then he called out again.

Then he came closer, was right below me out there on those big, flat rocks. Then I heard my name. That was a shocker. I rarely hear my name because on the radio I'm referred to as Coolwater. And, naturally, the tourists don't know me from Adam—or Eve.

Of course, I'm sure you've guessed it by now. The jerk in the pickup was not a jerk; he was my husband. And he was driving a new truck, a white one. Actually, he'd bought it because I'd written how horrible the road was and he was worried that the old truck wouldn't make it. And that's how things go sometimes, but sometimes they go better than others, especially when you're riding in a new pickup.

Looking Out

RAY OBERMAYR

DURING THE SUMMER OF 1956, I was a fire lookout on Thorn Creek Butte in the Boise National Forest. My regular job was teaching art at Idaho State University. We received only nine paychecks a year, so a summer job was an absolute necessity. I applied, was hired, and reported for work, with my wife and two small boys, at the Cottonwood Ranger Station on June 1.

The main man there, the district ranger, was a fellow named Woodrow Dupe, "Woody," of course. He pronounced the last name "Dupay." This is down-home Idaho. If a name when pronounced as spelled proves embarrassing, change it to sound nicer. For instance, we have a congressman in southeast Idaho named Crapo, pronounced "Craypo." Well, Woody was no dupe. He was on the end of the stick that does the duping. He lived with his family in a rustically elegant Forest Service house of many rooms and worked in a large office where he dutifully spent each day inventing paper busywork for himself and his underlings.

Dick Fischer was the assistant ranger. He became one of my heroes, and remains so to this day. The man could do anything. He could operate, maintain, and repair any kind of equipment—backhoes, bulldozers, road graders, dredges, telephones, radios, you name it. He read books. He could roll a cigarette with one hand while riding his dappled gray mare at a fast trot. Dick didn't look like a hero. He was small and wiry, very quiet. He never spoke at meetings. Woody did all the talking, but when anyone had a question it was always addressed to Dick. He was a logistical genius. He could plan an attack on a fire, on the spot, get the men and equipment in place quicker than anyone else, and put out the fire. Dick became famous eventually and commanded crews on all the biggest western fires. But he could never get a G.S. rating higher than assistant ranger because he hadn't gone to forestry school and had no degree like Woody's.

The summer crew at Cottonwood was made up of Mormon forestry students from Utah State University. They were okay, but noisy. Most were away from the scrutiny of their bishops for the first time, so they drank a lot of beer every night and all day Saturday and Sunday. In a few years, one of them would be Dick's boss.

Bear Valley Creek was once one of the best trout streams in the country. It ran through a ranch owned by Dick's family, homesteaded by his grandparents and where he grew up, learning all those things that Woody never dreamed of in forestry school. During World War II, while Dick was in the marines off in the Pacific, the land was condemned out from under his two aging parents and purchased by the government. The government reprivatized the valley by selling it to a big corporation for a dollar. The corporation put a dredge in the stream to suck the uranium out, tore everything up, poisoned the water and the land, and left it that way. Now, many years later, the government is spending large sums in an attempt to clean it up.

Cowboy Jack was a year-round employee of the Forest Service. In the summer he worked at Cottonwood, in the winter at headquarters in Boise. Cowboy Jack looked like a hero, wore a big white Stetson, and owned a beautiful sorrel mare. He was about as smart as Woody but luckily never went to college, so he remained just an ordinary worker. Cowboy Jack was tall and handsome with blond, curly hair. He behaved as though he were acting in a western epic, always posing, giving you his good side to look at, just in case someone might have a camera around.

On June 1 the lookout was still inaccessible because of a glacierlike field of ice, so I was put to work with the rest of the crew, fixing up things around the station. Then Cowboy Jack and I were sent out to clear fire trails. Dick thought this would give me a clear idea of the drainages visible from Thorn Creek Butte. He was right. But working with Jack was something else indeed. Our job was to clear a swath through the timber wide enough for a loaded pack animal and to shore up places on the sidehills where the trail had washed out.

Jack and I each had a mount and a pack mule to lead. Jack rode his sorrel and I had an old bay gelding with three white socks, strong but gentle, just right for me. Both mules were smart and answered to their names. Jack's was a jenny named Jenny. Philip was my mule. We got along well, and I developed a real affection for him during our time together. Jack's sorrel came in heat during one of our trips and Philip got a little skittish, but other than that he always did his work well. Philip had eyes for the pretty mare, but biology made it impossible for their affair to be anything but an Abelard and Heloise relationship. We gave the horses and mules a coffee can of oats in the morning. We covered ourselves and gear with the pack tarps at night to keep away the dew. When it got light, Philip would stick his head under the tarp and nuzzle me awake, oats on his mind. He didn't mess with Jack, probably sensing the typical cowboy's prejudice against mules. Some years later, when we owned a ranch near Pocatello, I tried to find Philip, looking to buy him. But Dick was off fighting fires in California, Woody had been promoted to a desk job in D.C., and there was no one around who knew Philip. They thought I was crazy. I guess at this point I should make a comparison between Philip's intelligence and common sense and that of the run-of-the-mill Forest Service bureaucrat, but enough has been said already; redundant.

Well, I was the greenest of greenhorns, the tenderest of anybody with feet. I had lived in the woods of Wisconsin and the Michigan Upper Peninsula, but I knew nothing of mountains or horses. So Cowboy Jack and I set off on our first trail trip, my family watching my unsteady departure. The boys took me for a big-shot cowboy, but Lorna knew better. I had never been on a horse before. The first day's trail ran along the North Fork of the Boise River. At times it was very narrow. The mules' packs scraped on the upside, the downside a thousand feet to the river. I was scared spitless, but I had the good sense, with no help from Cowboy Jack, to tie the reins to the saddle horn and close my eyes. I didn't try to steer the bay. He knew how to get through those sticky places. He didn't want to fall any more than I did. He knew what he was doing. We did have a minor rodeo when I got Philip's lead rope under the gelding's tail. Luckily we were on a flat. I managed to stay on and felt good on horseback for the first time. Philip watched and didn't buck off his pack, which he had done several times before. Much later, after we had our own animals, I came to understand that Jack hadn't fastened the diamond-hitched pack to Philip's saddle properly. Philip was uncomfortable.

I hated the Forest Service because it was so much like the army. I learned during four years in the service that the people who won World War II were the draftees from the Midwest, South, and West, farm and ranch boys who knew how to work tools and machinery, who could fix stuff, with baling wire if necessary. They knew that manufacturers' claims and instructions on how to assemble, run, and maintain equipment were mostly BS and had to be tempered with common sense or ignored. They coined the absolutely accurate saying "There are two ways of doing things: the army way and the right way." Whenever the risks were not too great, the farm and ranch boys ignored the officers' instructions and procedural regulations and just went right on ahead and won the war. The same work conditions prevailed in the Forest Service. Dick's persistence and skill at circumventing Forest Service regulations were heroic. It required heroism and heroic measures to do things properly in the "Fourcervice," as they say in Idaho.

Well, Cowboy Jack and I headed into the mountains with our animals and gear. The first obstruction we came to was a tree across the trail, a big one about four feet in diameter. We unlimbered our two-man crosscut saw. The steel part was rolled up and tied to Philip's pack. The wood handles were separate and had to be attached each time the saw was used. The station had a number of chain saws, but Woody said there was no money in his budget for chain saw gas and oil. Cottonwood Ranger Station was broke. He said it was all he could do to squeeze out enough money for such necessary items as his brand new office furniture and his new adding machine. So we crosscut through a lot of trees.

The saw, a true instrument of torture, was a bit longer than six feet. The steel was sharp as a razor. I had cut logs in the woods of northern Michigan, so I knew how to work a two-man saw. So did Jack, I soon found out. With one man on each side of the log, the saw teeth resting lightly on the bark, you alternated pulling the teeth toward you and then slacking off, just guiding the saw while your partner pulled. Then it came your turn to pull. It can be fun after you get a rhythm going, and the saw seems almost to work by itself, humming along, sending out an aroma of pine dust. It didn't work that way with Jack. At first I thought Jack was a victim of that "white man he-man" malady—no rhythm. But soon I saw that Jack wasn't pulling. He was just moving his arms back and forth. So I didn't push after I pulled. The saw stopped. But Jack knew me. He probably figured that if he persisted he could get me to do the pushing as well as pulling. My German Lutheran upbringing would not allow me to slack off, so I supplied the power to cut all the logs. We had to make two cuts in each log. This was tricky because you had to place wedges just right so that the saw wouldn't bind. After the two cuts were made, the center piece had to be rolled off the trail. Very often this was when the real work began. We hunted up poles for pry bars and wracked our brains for every principle of leverage to get the damned center piece rolling down the hill, but we always did it. With proper gear, Philip could have pulled those chunks of log out easily. A logger would have laughed to see us busting our guts so foolishly.

The Forest Service had manuals of procedures and equipment for everything imaginable. Just like in the army, they seemed to be written by people who had never been in the field and had only seen the equipment on a drawing board. The language was atrocious, like those translations from the Japanese instructing you how to assemble your kids' Christmas presents. These manuals were known as "the Book," and everyone was expected to "go by the Book."

According to the Book, we were to attend a safety meeting every Monday morning at seven o'clock, one hour before our usual starting time. At these meetings we were told how not to cut ourselves with axes or bump our heads, and to be sure to wear our hard hats when popping corn. The Book also said that when on trail work, we should begin the day at seven and work till six instead of five. The first morning Jack and I were on the trail, I felt something nudging me at about six. Thinking it was Philip wanting his oats, I told the source of the nudging to buzz off and leave me alone. The nudging continued and my language got worse. Finally I stuck my head out from under the tarp, and there was Cowboy Jack wanting to hold a safety meeting at six o'clock, just the two of us in the wilderness, thirty miles from the nearest road! Needless to say, I didn't attend Jack's meeting. Neither did Philip. That was the last talk of safety meetings we heard out of Jack.

Dick planned our trail work so we'd wind up each day at a place with grass and water for the stock. The country we traversed was as beautiful as anything anywhere. Alone, so far from man-made America, we were in our own private Idaho. Since I was exhausted from cross-cutting, quitting time was heavenly. We'd unsaddle the horses, unpack the mules, and let them drink. They'd roll to scratch their backs, fart and grunt, and get up and shake, flexing their sensitive hides in waves that rippled over their powerful bodies. We'd lay back and have a smoke. Then maybe cut a slender willow pole and catch some fish to liven up our meal of surplus army rations. We carried lines and hooks with us. Bait was grasshoppers, or crawly creatures we found under rocks. There were lots of six-inch brook trout, which were delicious broiled over coals. After supper we'd hobble the animals and build up the fire. Jack would tell self-aggrandizing whoring or drinking stories. Of course he was a great cocksman. I'd watch the stars, a spectacular display in this high country, get drowsy, turn in, rest my tired muscles till Philip wanted his oats.

Jack's going by the Book caused us trouble. The Book said we should work from seven till six, with a short break at noon. The animals were working too, or standing tied while we crosscut. We worked straight through till Book quitting time. Later, when I had my own horses, I learned what every mountainman knows: If you want your stock to stay around at night, you must stop early in the afternoon at a place with grass and water. The animals will eat their fill and sleep when you do. But we stopped by the Book, and the hungry animals, even though hobbled, wandered off, grazing. Philip, the union steward, led them to a guard station where they'd all led an easy life before, lots of grass and water, no packs, no two-hundred-pound horses' asses sitting on top of them.

Jack and I woke up horseless, afoot. We followed their trail till we knew it was hopeless, came back to camp, tied our goods up in a tree, and sat down to study the map. The rendezvous point, where we were to meet Dick and the trucks in two days' time, was forty miles away. We set off, hoofing it. We made it on time. The trucks were a welcome sight as we descended the last sidehill to the hoots and jeers of the waiting crew. Somehow Jack succeeded in laying the blame for the fiasco on me. I don't know how he did it, but Cowboy Jack couldn't screw up, could he? I was pooped, had worn out my new pair of Red Wings on those shale sidehills, and went home to the warmth of my family and slept.

Two days later, Great Day in the Morning! Dick came in and said the fire season was on and it was time to go up to the lookout. No more crosscutting with Cowboy Jack! Dick led the way in a truck and we followed in our station wagon. After a lot of switchbacks we were in sight of the lookout, but there was a huge bank of ice in the way, covering the road. Dick revved up his chain saw and cut out blocks of ice, clearing the road. He opened the lookout, turned on the radio, gave us some final instructions, and went back to Cottonwood. The ice field extended to the shade of a giant Douglas fir. It was our refrigerator for the rest of the summer.

There we were on Thorn Creek Butte. The locals called it Baldy or Bald Mountain, and it was. The trees stopped about a hundred yards from the top, just below the garage, a neat white building used to store worn-out equipment of all descriptions. The Book made it practically impossible to get rid of anything. Disposal required so many forms and so much paperwork that even Woody balked. The two story lookout rose from the very tip of Baldy. The sleeping quarters and storeroom made up the ground floor. The lookout proper was the second floor. The roofed balcony, all around, gave it a rather elegant look. And the view, north, south, east, west: the searing Owyhee desert, the snow-peaked Sawtooths, the green-forested Twin Lakes, and the half-green, half-brown Grimes Peak, never the same two days running, sometimes changing dramatically moment to moment.

Our first day was quite an initiation. A lightning storm came up. I was recording strikes and watching for smoke. My family and I were all upstairs when it struck: a blinding flash, a crackling sound, the pungent smell of ozone. Our hair stood straight up. We were dazed at first, then frightened when we realized we had taken a direct hit. I had the feeling like just after an artillery shell hit and you realized that all your limbs bent the right way and there weren't any holes where there weren't supposed to be. We all fell into a fit of giggling. The boys were wide-eyed. They'd sure have something for show and tell. The lookout had a lightning-proof stool with glass insulators for feet. The Book said that if family or visitors were present during a lightning storm, no one but the official lookout was to get up on the stool. Oh, the Forest Service was so much like the army, in this case showing the same disregard for the safety of civilians. My army experience, which included time at the Fort Sheridan guardhouse and combat overseas, had been traumatic. Working for the Forest Service reawakened that trauma and induced depression, which I had to fight hard to overcome. I had to remind myself of significant differences: Forest Service fools could take up your time with nonsense, but the effect was merely inconvenience or discomfort. In the army, fools could deal you life or death. Keep perspective!

Less serious than reawakened army traumas was the simple aggravation at having to do things wrong. My instinct of workmanship was violated by the Forest Service Book. Directive-issuing bosses generally don't understand that we, their underlings, want to do our work well, and take pride in succeeding. They underestimate us.

My vision of living on the lookout in splendid isolation, contemplating the glories of nature from the balcony, painting watercolors perhaps, writing, reading, was shattered by two factors. First, Woody, of course.

Woody was a devout Christian, a lay preacher, in fact. He conducted prayer meetings on Sunday morning. He was an Early Day Christian, what would nowadays be called Born Again. But he had little success getting that hungover crew of Later Day Saints to attend his services. Woody believed passionately that an idle mind is the Devil's workshop. An idle mind is one not engaged in some prescribed Book project. A mind engaged in contemplation, reading, writing, thinking is idle. With my mind in mind, Woody brought up a load of white paint and instructed me to paint the lookout and garage, which I did. The lookout took a lot of time because of the many small windowpanes, pains after a while. I worked hard and thought it looked pretty good.

Woody brought up some more paint and told me to paint everything again. "It takes two coats," he said. I put on the second coat. Woody brought up another pickup load of paint and told me to do it again. I told him that the paint was so thick now that any more would probably chip off.

"No," he said. "We have some pretty hard winters up here."

I began to think he was jiving me, playing some kind of joke like when an old-timer sends a novice to the warehouse for a board stretcher. Well, I said no more but hid the paint behind some junk in the garage. When Woody came up with more paint, he looked things over carefully and said I was doing a good job. Positive reinforcement.

"One more coat ought to do it," he said.

In looking for another hiding place, I uncovered a whole bunch of cans of white paint with the lids busted off by the frost the winters before. Woody had also attended to the previous lookouts' idle minds. The painting charade took most of the summer.

The other factor I hadn't counted on was that I was not the loner I supposed. I thought I'd relish being away from everything and everyone, not having to talk to anyone except my family. Wrong. I am a gregarious person. I need people. I love casual conversations with strangers. One of us, either my wife or I, had to be at the lookout at all times. Usually when we needed groceries, Lorna would go down to town. I found myself trying to think up reasons why I should go instead, so I could talk to the grocer about the weather, or have a beer and shoot the shit with rednecked loggers at the tavern in Idaho City. Well, know thyself.

So the arrival of old Pete and Ignacio was welcome. They were Basque sheepherders who came up with a band of sheep—five hundred of them. Pete was seventy, Nacio eighteen. Pete had been in this country for many years, but Nacio was a recent arrival. They came from villages only six miles apart in Spain, but they couldn't speak to each other because Pete spoke only Basque and English and Nacio spoke only Spanish and French, having grown up in Franco's Spain when it was forbidden to teach the Basque language in the schools. Fortunately, I knew a little French, and my translating from French to English and back was their only method of communicating. We had many hilarious misunderstandings. The sheep camp was on French Creek, just a quarter mile away, so we saw a lot of them. They were both very polite and considerate men, and they became our friends.

Pete and Nacio were each paid $200 a month plus keep. Their groceries were brought up every two weeks and consisted of the usual sheepherder's fare: dry beans and rice, various canned goods, and gallons of red wine. Their meat was lamb. They always brought some for us whenever they slaughtered, and usually dropped off a jug of wine too. That was the first time my family and I had ever eaten lamb. We roasted or broiled it over coals. It was delicious. Just a whiff of cooking lamb now brings these two good men to mind.

The sheep were owned by a corpulent, Stetsoned, silver-haired man named Nicholson. He lived in a log palace, almost a castle, on Moores Creek. I mean it was huge. Nicholson came up with the trucks when the first five hundred sheep arrived. Woody came too. We had a meeting, Woody, Nicholson, and I. Part of my duties was to keep track of the sheep to see whether the terms of Nicholson's grazing permit were obeyed. Woody told me to report daily on this, via the radio. The herders were to take the sheep on a route Woody showed me on the map. The route brought them back to French Creek after a week. They were to rest a day, then set out again for a week on a different route, the idea being to avoid overgrazing any part of the area.

Two days later, trucks brought another band of five hundred sheep. I reported that to Woody. Pete and Nacio took the thousand sheep out each day and brought them back at night. They merely circled the butte instead of following the week-long assigned route. I felt bad. I thought the herders were doing that simply because it was easier. I had a talk with them. They told me they were following Nicholson's orders. I reported this to Woody. His secretary called me back and said not to worry. This went on all summer, and I reported everything to Woody every day. I was told not to worry. I guess the sheep gained a lot more weight by not having to walk so far. But they turned the entire butte to powder, and of course, the next spring runoff washed out the road. Neither Nicholson nor Woody footed the bill to replace it. The taxpayers did.

Bucking season came on while those thousand sheep were milling around Thorn Creek Butte. Bawling and baaing like you've never heard, and stink like you've never smelled. Dust too.

I was required to tour the catwalk every fifteen minutes, but this was not a chore. It was always a pleasure to survey that gorgeous panorama. I made the usual beginner's mistakes, reporting smoke from the dump on Grimes Peak, dust from vehicles on dirt roads, and early-morning mist that looked like smoke. Gradually I learned what was smoke and what wasn't, and where it was not supposed to be. It felt good to be doing something we all thought worthwhile. We were part of the outfit that was helping Smokey the Bear and Ranger Rick save the forests. There were no major fires in the Boise Forest that year, but a lot of little ones, mostly from lightning. I was surprised to learn that almost all forest fires are lightning caused. They are rarely bad ones because they are usually in higher altitudes and burn themselves out quickly. The bad ones are often caused by hunters, campers, tourists, and all manner of cigarette smokers.

August 31, the lookout in a cloud, we seemed to be adrift in gossamer white. Silence, deep quiet. The cloud gradually dispersed and the surrounding peaks became islands in a silent white sea. Large, wet snowflakes drifted to the ground, continuing throughout the day until the snow was two feet deep. Fire season was over. All the lookouts were called in. Dick radioed us to come on down. We stowed the lookout gear, went down to Cottonwood, took care of some final paperwork, and headed home.

All in all I'm glad I was a lookout. I'm even glad I worked for the "Fourcervice." I learned my way around the mountains, breathed clean air in the midst of fantastic beauty. I learned to saddle, bridle, and hobble a horse, and to sit on one without falling off. I learned to tie a diamond hitch. I met some very good people and animals. I learned that I was not a loner. I learned that Cowboy Jack and Woody are ubiquitous, that there are too many of them in this world, not enough Dicks and Philips, and not enough people who can tell the difference.

Against This Ground
excerpt 1

DONNA ASHWORTH

Woody Mountain, Friday and Saturday, May 18 and 19, 1990
Isolation was still possible in Arizona. All her life she had lived with a sky that was three-fourths of the landscape, big enough to fill a century, and mountains that rose on every horizon. She had grown up learning in unpeopled miles where danger was only natural, not malicious. The isolation of a mountaintop fire lookout job suited her.

Ten miles away, Flagstaff with its forty-five thousand plus people was a toy town that occupied only 15 degrees on her fire-finder circle of 360. On her mountain, there was quiet and time and room enough to grow tall as a sycamore tree if she could manage to learn how. Worth the effort anyway.

It was spring. The Arizona sun was long past equinox and approaching solstice, burning almost as high overhead as it would all year. In the drought months, Pacific storms had as usual swung north into Canada, and the storm track along the Mexican border had disappeared. An upper level ridge capped the West. Cloudless days stretched into monotony, day after day of brilliant, empty sky.

Wind blew constantly, roaring past the walls, humming against the steel girders of the old tower, whistling around the window frames in a noise that seldom stopped. The tower felt alive and pulsing. She kept the windows fastened shut in the mornings and sat against the east wall watching the tops of pines sway below her. In her glass room she was free in any weather for eighty miles in all directions, from the Painted Desert to the mountains west of Prescott.

From that height the whole Coconino forest stretched away, ridges rolling in waves to the horizon in succeeding shades of green, color upon color, blue fifteen miles away, pale blue-gray at eighty. Shadows outlined canyons in morning light, and details of the sides of distant mountains were distinct. As the sun crossed the sky, contours and canyons eased away to reappear again under afternoon shadow in a different palette of green, brown, blue.

Traces of snow outlined ridges high on the peaks she could see from her north window. Wind was cold. On the mountain, buds on oak trees were so tightly furled that the branches looked skeletal and brown among the pines, but the clump of aspen on the northeast slope was turning from white to green. Elderberry bushes were putting on new leaves. In sunny patches a few grasses were showing green close to the ground.

Ravens and swallows flashed past on the wind. Hawks faced into it, hanging motionless for minutes at a time.

With her binoculars she watched their eyes, dark and intent, searching the ground far beneath. Something about those eyes. With a hawk there was no chance of a friendly relationship.

Below the cover of the treetops, an orange-yellow tanager sat on a moving branch, and small gray-brown birds fluttered from limb to limb. When the wind abated for a moment, she could hear their voices and the quarreling of male broad-tailed hummingbirds as they defended from each other the red feeders she had hung from the eaves of her cabin on the ground.

She had a ritual. Sitting on the doorstep in the light of the setting sun, she unbraided her hair and brushed it. She loved the way each strand shone gold and then copper and then almost silver as sun moved lower and vanished behind the hills. Shadows on their eastern sides really did turn purple when the light was on the horizon. It was a magic time, the transformation into night. Curling the ends of her hair around her finger, she watched until stars appeared. Maybe she could learn to shine like evening.

Wind blowing from the southwest in daylight came from the Pacific off the Baja coast. Wind at night, in a black sky under the stars, rushed past from someplace vast and unknown, hissing through the pines with a purpose that had nothing to do with humans. While she lay in bed reading Annie Dillard or Wallace Stegner, light from her battery-powered reading lamp escaped the edges of the book to which it was clipped and illuminated the ceiling. Bats and mice and owls and skunks and coyotes were busy on the dark mountain hunting food, but they made no sound in the unending wind, and she did not hear them. Nor did she listen. She was not afraid of them. Why should she be?

Sometimes in the morning, cooking breakfast on the propane stove, she looked out past yellow curtains to see an Abert squirrel traveling through the pines, leaping onto branches, clutching with its clever feet, riding the flex and bounce, then hurrying on. She had seen a small gray fox just outside at the basin she kept filled beside her water pump and whispered, "You pretty thing," as it trotted away down the slope and disappeared. Once there had been a four-toed print in the moist earth beside the basin, smaller than a baby's hand.

The lookout job was not solitude. Life swirled around her in every size and color. She wondered at the occasional hiker who asked, "Don't you get lonesome up here all by yourself?" and couldn't find an answer.

When interfering types said, "You know, you can't hide up here forever," she wanted to say, "I don't know why not. It's an island of safety in a world rapidly going crazy. War in Lebanon. Terrorism. Rape of children. Inner cities." But she didn't. People weren't interested in private sanity. They were interested in group.

Worst was the question "What do you do for entertainment without electricity?" Jeesh! Didn't anyone read anymore? Or walk? Or sing?

Friday morning an older man, seventy or so, climbed the tower and knocked at the trapdoor, the first visitor of the season. For fifteen minutes he sat in the lookout chair and asked the usual questions.

"How long do you stay up here? How much money do you make?" Suddenly he moved to her side of the tower, saying nothing, his mouth spread in a stiff smile. Eyes blank as a doll's. She was on the sill-high window seat behind the fire finder, her only barrier against visitors. He stood less than two feet away.

Slow and deliberate, he pulled a knife from his left pants pocket, reached across the bulge of his paunch, and opened the blade half out, watching her. Sure that she noticed, he pulled the knife full open, held it in front of him pointing toward her, meaning something, and began to rub his thumb back and forth across the steel. His eyes did not leave her face.

She looked away from him out across treetops through twenty-five miles of open air to mountains sharp-edged as cardboard cutouts. "Put it away." Her pistol was below in the cabin. She had not expected danger in the tower in daytime. Oh, shit. Double shit.

He hesitated a moment. Then, still slow and deliberate, still silently grinning, he folded the knife, returned it to his pocket, and went back to the lookout chair.

A minute earlier he had said his wife was out of town.

She asked, "She's gone to visit relatives?"

"Her sister." He seemed excited.

As he talked, she picked up the pencil she had sharpened that morning and held it in front of her on the fire finder. Her white sleeves were stark against the green circle of the map. You old bastard. If you come at me again, I'll hit your eyes. Grab that white hair, pull back your head, jab up under your jaw. She did not hear what he was saying. When he paused, she asked about the grown sons he had mentioned earlier.

The tower was only seven feet square. The fire finder occupied an eighteen-inch block in the middle. She couldn't move without losing its shelter, not even to open the trapdoor and order him to leave. She looked past him out the window at the hawk soaring above the ridge.

Finally he stood. "Well, guess I'll be going. Don't wanta wear out my welcome. I'll be back next week." He smiled as he went down through the opening in the floor.

Bruised was how it felt. She dropped the trapdoor behind him and locked it. That's it. That's it. No more Good Host. You can sit in offices in town writing memos all you want to, not another man gets in here unless he brings women and children with him.

He had defecated in her cathedral. Violated her mind. Robbed a little more from her that she could not grow back. For as long as she could remember, she had been afraid of men in cars, on trails, behind her at the teller machine. She was sick of anonymous violence. Women made it personal, women spoke their violence. She had learned to be afraid of what women might say. A woman could deliver a mortal wound without raising an arm. She felt alive and sure of who she was only when she was alone.

He had told her his name. After he left, she wrote a report of the incident for the district law enforcement officer. She did not anticipate much help. Women in the Forest Service were expected to take care of themselves. Hurray for equality.

She had another ritual. At noon she went down for lunch break carrying fifteen pounds of Forest Service radio. When she reached the bottom of the stairs, she set the radio on the ground, turned and ran up the first flight again as fast as she dared, hands on the rails, braids thumping on her back. At the landing she turned around, "The Elephant's Child went on, a little warm but not at all astonished," and ran down again. She did it every day at noon. And again at five o'clock so as not to end the season with the shape of a slug. Probably puzzled the ground squirrels no end.

The new patrolman drove up the mountain road that afternoon. She heard his hundred-gallon pumper truck when it came through the gate half a mile down, put an old postcard into her book, and watched as he parked below and got out. In the air forty-five feet above him, she saw that his cheddar-red hair was thinning at the crown.

"Have to let the Forest Service in. I wonder if I could put up a sign: Dogs Allowed—No Humans." She reached over to the little battery radio on the windowsill and switched off the university station down in town, stopping Galway's flute in the middle of Lloyd Webber's "Memory." It was the first nine notes she liked best anyway.

His fire boots made the tower vibrate as he climbed the stairs. Unlocking the trapdoor, she stepped across, held it open and waited, wary, as his thin hair came up through the opening.

"Hi."

"That's quite a climb—catch my breath." He looked out at the Peaks. "Is that the Naval Observatory?"

"Yes."

"It looks like a big, white marble from here."

She had forgotten his name. While he recovered, she glanced at the pin on his uniform shirt. Charles Owens. Tall and stick-thin, nose large and crooked, red skin with a wine-dark birthmark on the left side of his face. The first time she had seen him in the ranger station, she had been startled for a moment and tried not to let it show, tried to look at him and smile, wondering whether every woman faced him with a strained expression. It was one of her faults—she was too quick with sympathy for imagined grief. At the age of seven she had crowded half a dozen dolls into her bed at night, afraid to hurt the feelings of any by leaving a few out. There hadn't been room to turn over.

"Here, sit down." She gestured to the tower's only chair and moved around behind the fire finder, keeping it between them.

"Thanks, I will. Old Hot Shot motto: Why stand when you can sit? How's it going? Need anything?"

"Batteries for the radio. I haven't any spares. Without a radio I'm useless."

"I guess. You could see smoke, but you couldn't tell anybody about it. Unless you're a powerful long-distance shouter?" His smile made lines crinkle from the corners of his eyes. "I'll bring some up right away. Anything else?"

"Would you please take this note in to Kent? I had some trouble I wanted him to know about. You could call it a safety report."

"You have a safety problem up here? Anything I can fix? That's part of my job."

She pulled forward a braid and began making a curl in the end of it. Looking at her hands, the map board, the radio, briefly at his face, she told him about the knife and the man's promise to come back. "I wondered whether Kent could check with the police for a record of his causing trouble. Maybe it's silly. But I'd like to take some action. I can't just sit up here and flinch at strange noises." She shrugged one shoulder.

"Sure, I'll deliver it." He folded the paper and slipped it into his pocket notebook. "I don't know what's wrong with some guys, maybe they're getting in touch with the sicko within."

She managed a laugh. "I was trying to be nice. He said he was sixty-nine and retired and his wife was out of town, and I didn't want him to think I thought he wasn't worth my time. I must have a head full of popcorn."

"I wouldn't call it that, no, you kept cool in a sticky situation. You did fine. It's hard to tell these days who you can afford to be nice to."

"Isn't that the truth!" At least his voice wasn't homely. "Thanks. You have a way of changing minus into plus."

His grin showed all his teeth. "Natural talent, but I try to be modest about it, you know, don't want to be swamped with appeals at tax time."

There was a loud thump somewhere down the tower. His face tensed. "What was that?"

"Wind caught a loose board on the third landing, I think. It stimulates my imagination something wonderful."

The next afternoon he was back, climbing in a noisy thirty-mile-an-hour wind with a box of batteries and a small paper sack. "Man! It's cold once you get above the trees."

"Not in this little glass box. Here, I'll take those batteries. Thanks."

"Glad to. You do get solar gain in here all right."

She moved around to the shady side and slid across the window seat until she was behind the fire finder. "Sit down."

"Listen, I—oh, thanks." He settled onto the edge of the chair, sun through the window bright on the shoulder seam of his shirt. "I gave your report on the guy with the knife to Kent, but I don't know what he'll do beyond keeping it on file. He just said to tell you that you don't have to let people in if you don't want to. So I hope you don't mind, but I looked the guy up in the phone book and called him. I told him the district has a full description and he'd better not come back. Maybe it wasn't my place . . ."

"No. Oh, no. That was wonderful. Thank you so much." She looked full into his face, trying not to avoid the side with the birthmark. "I couldn't decide what I should do, especially if he showed up after hours."

"He claims you misunderstood, he got the knife out to clean his fingernails, and he was surprised when you asked him to put it away."

Bullshit! "That old liar!"

"I figured you were here and you knew, so I told him not to come back again even to apologize."

"That coward! Just an innocent old man accused unjustly, and I'm the guilty one. The victim is always the guilty one."

"Yeah, well, that's how I figured it. So I warned him off."

"You're—that's really—I'm very grateful. I'll calm down in a minute. Maybe." She felt exposed revealing anger. Revealing anything. "It's a relief to know somebody called him."

"You don't mind? You never know these days. Some women get insulted. Like you're calling them helpless or something. Makes you hesitate to try your Superman act. You can feel pretty silly standing there in your cape and skivvies, flexing your muscles, you know, when some woman says, 'Stop that! Who needs you?'" His face assumed a cartoon pose that made her laugh.

"No, that's not right. Helping's not a put-down. 'It isn't much fun for one, but two can stick together, says Pooh, says he.'" She stopped. Oops, that sounded intimate. Damn.

He took a black cylinder out of the sack he held and offered it to her. "Here, I picked up a can of Mace in case you'd like to have it. Creep repellent. The flap—no, turn it the other way so you have a pistol grip—you slide your thumb under the flap and push the red button. Try not to shoot into the wind."

She laughed. "This is great! I do want it, I've never had one. It even has a serial number."

"You're up here all alone with jerks running loose in the woods. Gets worse all the time—they reproduce every sixty days like jackrabbits. I thought maybe you'd like to, you know, have some defense you could carry in your pocket."

"How much was it? I'll pay you."

"I'd absorb it as my contribution to the war on crime. But it was twenty dollars. Is that too much? Better read the directions. See, on the side?"

"'Use extreme care with intoxicated, drugged, demented, enraged, or other persons having reduced sensitivity to pain.' I didn't know about that."

"Yep." He nodded. "Reduced sensitivity probably takes in about half the population, although they might not know it."

His eyes were washed-out blue. He seemed nice, especially when he smiled. Except that there are endless varieties of psychological predation. When it came to people, anything she decided was usually wrong.

This is an edited excerpt from the novel *Against This Ground* by Donna Ashworth.

Against This Ground excerpt 2

DONNA ASHWORTH

Woody Mountain, Friday, June 22, 1990

Solstice sun was midway in its seasonal trek up and down the horizon. Temperature at the mountain's eight thousand feet was 85 degrees. Using a spray bottle to keep herself covered with evaporating water, she had her windows wide open, her shirt off, her hair pinned up, a hat tilted to shade her eyes from the glare. Violet-green swallows flashed around the tower. One zoomed in through an open window and out the other side.

"Show off," she said.

Relative humidity was down to five percent, the forest the driest it'd been all season.

Although she filled the feeders every morning, hummingbirds drank them down by afternoon. Then the little birds buzzed into the tower to inform her and insist that she do something about it. Or so it seemed. The tiny green bodies hovered in front of her face, their wings fanning her cheeks. She turned her head and they moved to hang before her eyes again. When she herded them to the windowsill and closed her hands around them, they waited, unmoving, their black eyes lustrous as beads, until she released them out the window.

Nobody would believe me if I told this. Maybe Charley would. Anyone else would say a hummingbird's brain is too small to make connections. I'm not so different from other creatures, only a little less than kin.

Fire activity all over the West was still building, even though she herself hadn't seen smoke for days.

Charley arrived on the mountain out of schedule. When she heard him coming, she hurried to button her shirt and turn off a chamber orchestra playing Scarlatti, and then held the trapdoor open for him. He had a box of fresh batteries.

"Here you are. Compliments of the friendly folks at the ranger station. Also a batch of time sheets in case you were getting low. And Kent wants to know how's the level in your propane tanks?"

"I'll need a refill soon." She cleared the chair of blue yarn. "Sit down."

"What are you knitting?"

"A sweater for my mother. For Christmas. See?" She held it up.

"Looks complicated. Is it hard to do?"

"Not when you get it figured out. It's like riding a bicycle, easy once you know how." She gathered the books on the window seat into a stack to make room for herself.

"What are you reading?"

"History. Hunting for ideas."

"You're hunting ideas? What kind?"

He was the first man she had known for years who didn't feel like a foreigner. "Now don't laugh at me." She smiled, embarrassed. "I said I wanted life to have more meaning than an endless round of teaching? It's a sophomoric question, I know, but it bothers me. So I look for what other people have thought, anything to give me a place to start." She held up her hand to stop his grin. "Lit major—looks for answers to life in books."

"I didn't say that."

"You know what I've been thinking?"

"Couldn't guess."

"Book history is usually about power that did more harm than good. There's no help there. Life doesn't have meaning just because you've bounced your ego off a lot of people. The impulse to power, over anything, is more immoral than all the traditional sins. Maybe I should study hermits."

"Like monks?"

"They wouldn't have to be religious. At least not as we think of it. In China a thousand years ago mountains were the natural place to search for the Tao, and scholars retreated to them, or thought they should. Lun Yu said the virtuous find pleasure in mountains."

"Sounds like a philosophy for a lookout all right."

"Did you ever notice how much of Chinese painting is landscape with mountains?"

"Can't say as I have."

"Well, it's a lot. And somewhere in the painting there's often a little open hut and a hermit scholar reading a book."

"Looks pretty familiar, I bet."

"People find out what my job is and they say, 'What are you trying to do, be a hermit?' as if that's some kind of insult. To live with beauty like this daily"—she swept her hand in a half circle—"they can't know how spiritual it is."

He looked around and nodded, smiling.

"If you ever wanted to talk to God or minds from the past, this would be the place, not in a crowded church. So anyway, maybe I should study hermits. Maybe hermits are people who want their lives to have meaning but realize they can affect nothing but themselves. I don't know. I'm just thinking. Excuse me for getting off on a tirade."

His red hands were resting on his thighs. "My grandfather was a farmer, and I think his life had meaning. At least, he said he wanted his work to have meaning. But he wasn't a recluse. Everybody loved him. He worked hard, but he said it was good work. He never made much money." . . .

Woody Mountain, Monday, June 25 and 26, 1990, four days past summer solstice

Temperatures rose to 90 degrees plus in Flagstaff, on the deserts to 120. Relative humidity was still only 5 percent. With fire danger all over Arizona rated extreme, commercial logging and chain saw use in the forest had been curtailed for weeks. The pines on the mountain had a hot-weather smell. Half butterscotch, half turpentine. Sun did not reach the windowsill on the south wall of the tower. Flying ants on lavender wings emerged from holes in the ground, swarmed around the tower, lost their wings, and descended into the earth again. Creatures from Greek myth.

After lunch that Monday, she sat in her underwear on the window seat clothed in wind and sky, watching great white cumulus clouds balloon above the Peaks, swelling out of themselves. "Is there noise up there in the clouds when they do that?"

At 13:30 Baker Butte reported drift smoke coming up from below the Rim, close to the location of the big fire three weeks earlier. The man on Buck Mountain saw it too and radioed a cross, but she couldn't find it. A Blue Ridge range technician, out on the edge, said he could see fire half a mile to the south.

The Hopi dispatcher took control of the forest radio, his fire traffic taking precedence over everything else. He notified the fire boss on the Long Valley District of possible trouble and told him he had telephoned to the dispatcher on the Tonto. Within minutes he had six engines, two water tenders, two big Model 70s and a dozer on the road and was calling every five minutes for "any Coconino Hot Shot Crew." Drivers had taken empty buses to New Mexico a week earlier to bring the crews home when they were ready, but it was the first she had heard that they had been released and were on the road. She leaned out the window and complained to the trees. "Nobody ever tells lookouts anything."

By 13:40, with no Coconino unit on the Rim except that one range technician, who advised, "It's building, Mo, keep everything coming," another engine had been dispatched and so had both the Mormon Lake and Blue Ridge hose caches. The Long Valley fire boss radioed from his truck to ask whether the dispatcher could vacuum up any Indian crews. As they talked, she could hear a voice in the office on the telephone ordering air tankers and a lead plane. A second dozer was reported available, and a scramble started to find an operator for it.

At 13:51, with no answer from the Hot Shots on the road, the Stanislaus crew was ordered from the Kaibab. A patrolman was sent to the Rim road to direct public traffic away from danger, and north end units were moved to Happy Jack in the center of the forest and told to stand by. Her back turned to clouds white as soap suds above the peaks, she watched a monstrous black smoke billow up on the horizon and tilt toward the northeast.

The dispatcher reached the Flagstaff Hot Shots on the highway east of Winslow at 14:00 and diverted them south. At 14:07 the first units began to arrive at the Rim with people and water. At 14:10 the district fire boss radioed that fire was climbing fast in a strong wind and he doubted the Rim road would hold it. A group of summer houses was two miles from the front.

The pitch of voices was rising, and she was safe and barefoot. She listened as the Mormon Lake and Blue Ridge crews came within radio contact and were told to turn south, as the Forest Management Team was activated, as smoke jumpers were ordered from Cedar City. But even with her binoculars, she couldn't see the Tonto and Coconino Air Attack planes above the smoke.

Radio transmission from the fire was erratic. A voice would fade to nothing or cut out in midsentence, and the dispatcher asked the Moqui lookout to stay in her tower until further notice to relay. The fire boss on the Flagstaff district called to Woody Mountain and Elden. "Extend until dark."

When she went down the stairs at dusk under a quarter moon, her brain was ringing with the constant sound of voices with orders, requests, warnings. Barricades had been set up to block the Rim road. Air space above the fire had been closed to sightseers. Water trucks and caterers with food had been sent down the Happy Jack Road. She sat in the cabin listening to communications she half understood. By then the fire was burning in 120 acres below the Rim and 20 on top. Hundreds of people were there with tons of equipment. They would work all night, their voices dim in her sleep.

Just before she woke next morning, she dreamed of flapping her arms frantically to stay out of reach of the hands that were trying to grab her ankles and pull her down. There were calls from the fire on the radio. She opened her eyes, turned onto her back, and punched her pillows up to lie and listen. The voices were ordering people and more supplies or asking when they would arrive, but there was no detail to give her an idea of how things were going.

The sky she could see through the trees on the horizon beyond the Navajo Reservation, usually apricot pink at dawn, was orange brown with smoke. Windblown branches on trees outside made moving shadows on the wall. She knew that people on the fire line had probably not yet had any sleep.

As air warmed, radio traffic from the Rim became erratic again, with parts of sentences sounding and then breaking off. Sometimes she thought she could hear Coconino or Tonto people talking to each other. Apparently there were planes over the fire for a second day.

After breakfast when she carried the radio up into the tower, the column of black smoke still stood heavy on the horizon. Morning was breezy, warm, and clear with no sign of clouds. Bad weather for fire fighting. In the prime burning conditions after 10:00, danger increased, and the broken transmissions she could hear were more urgent.

"It's making a run! Start your back fire! Now! You've got two minutes!" Later: "You gonna be able to hold it?" Then silence for a while and suddenly: ". . . flames curling over the road! Pull back! Pull back!"

Wind picked up in the afternoon, blowing the roiling smoke off to the northeast across the Reservation. Sun burned through the west tower windows. "I wouldn't want that job for any money."

At one point she thought she heard a faint radio voice shout, "Deploy fire shelters!" She increased the volume, but there was nothing else. Fire shelters meant someone on the ground had been over-run. God. Oh God. It hurt to think of. A few minutes later she caught, ". . . crew is cut off."

She realized she hadn't heard Charley come into service in the morning, hadn't heard him on the radio all day. He was without a doubt down there. Everybody who could drive had gone down with a load of something. "Who?" she said aloud. "Who's cut off?"

Half an hour later she heard a dim call for hel-evac. And then the radio went silent again.

The solitary afternoon wore on with no news, no activity, no fires on the north end of the forest. A few clouds drifted through the sky, trailing shadows behind them across the trees, and dissipated. "Human bodies are so pitifully vulnerable. All those people on the fire, naked inside their clothing, facing towering flames with hoes and shovels." She was safe and comfortable and alone and out of things, too tense for reading. Wind was gusting at twenty-five to thirty.

At four o'clock the dispatcher called 4-3. "Van, I need to confirm that all Coconino people are above the Rim."

"That's affirmative, Mo."

"And all Coconino people are okay?"

"That's affirmative."

"Repeat: All Coconino people are above the Rim and unharmed?"

"Affirmative."

"Now what does that mean? Somebody below the Rim hurt? Is that where the crew was cut off?"

At the end of a day that had seemed longer than usual, she went down the stairs to the cabin. Setting the Forest Service radio on top of the refrigerator, she flipped a switch on her cassette radio for the evening news. The first words she heard were: ". . . six firefighters killed and five badly burned this afternoon as fifteen hundred people mounted an all-out assault on a five-thousand-acre wildfire that has destroyed fifty-seven cabins and threatened others northeast of Payson." She stood numb. Six dead? No. No.

The newscaster went on to talk of a fast-moving front throwing sparks out three-quarters of a mile ahead, of fifty Hot Shot crews, continuous drops of fire retardant from seven slurry bombers and water from six helicopters, but she dropped into a chair waiting for names. All up and down the Rim firefighters were silent, listening. Searchers reporting finding a hard hat and a body and part of a fire shelter. And another body. And another. Five men and one woman had died nearly instantly of inhaled, superheated air in what survivors called "a tidal wave of fire." Others had been carried out to hospitals.

"Who?" she whispered. The newscaster answered, "None of the victims were identified immediately by Tonto National Forest officials, who would say only that they were from two twenty-member crews."

"So that's what you meant—all Coconino people are above the Rim and unharmed. You knew about it then, hours ago. All our people with their tender, naked skin are safe. But there are families . . ." She sat and grieved for people she did not know, mourning centuries of individual death.

The fire seared her mind. It burned out of control for nearly a week, charring forty-five square miles of forest, destroying seventy-five homes, and involving twenty-four hundred fire fighters from several forests, people from the Rural Metro organization, sixty men from the Arizona National Guard, Southwest Indian Firefighter crews, and a crew from the Perryville Prison, all working shifts sometimes as long as thirty to forty hours. Suppression cost was seven and a half million dollars.

Temperatures in the southern part of the state had been above 120 degrees during those solstice days. There had been too many agencies on the ground for effective control, communications confusion, not enough radios to go around, fire behavior no one had experienced before. And always the wind rushing at Arizona out of the southwest.

This edited excerpt from *Against This Ground* recounts the Dude Fire of 1990, which took place in Arizona. The Rim referred to means that of the Mogollon Canyon south of Flagstaff. The victims were members of the Perryville Prison crew.

Pawnote on the Hoary Marmot: After Observation, Contemplation, and a Smattering of Research

R. LIGHTBULB WINDERS

I WOULDN'T CALL the hoary marmot beautiful, or even cute, though it has that awkward lack of proportion that some people kindly label as cuteness.

Blame it all on the tail. If you first settle your gaze on the marmot's head (though it's too small to allow much chance of intelligence), you'll find it handsomely black below the eyes, with trim bits of white about the nose and crown. The shoulders' long silver fur creates an elegant frosted effect as it grades into shorter black hair on the animal's front legs.

But the creature's posterior turns a sudden dirty yellow-brown that ruins the effect of all that has come before. And it flares so loutishly that the creature can't move without waddling. A naturalist aesthete could accept these defects, perhaps, if it weren't for the tail of that same ugly brown, fluffy at first sight, but tastelessly straight, free of expressive curl. Though it sometimes rises stiffly as a sign of annoyance, it usually trails meaninglessly behind, as out of place as a foxtail tacked to a bicycle fender.

I once dared touch a marmot's tail. I ventured slowly up behind one of the larger of the beasties that inhabit the meadows surrounding the fire lookout. The marmot ignored my presence, browsing unconcerned on anemones and lupines. Conscious of the creature's sharp teeth and irascible nature, I dared stretch out my hand only a moment and gingerly run my finger down the dun-colored hairs. The fur was coarse and unpleasant. My fantasy of taming him to curl on my mattress as a pillow at night immediately faded. So I had no regrets when the beast started in alarm and waddled away down the mountainside, removing his bristly hide forever from my grasp.

I don't wish to berate the hoary marmot, low minded and ludicrous as he may seem. Green Mountain belonged to the marmot long before the first fire lookout arrived in the beast's grazing lands, with a tent to pitch on the flowered ridge and a portable fire finder to prop on the summit rocks. That was in the days before the peak was blasted flat, before the little house was built on the cliff's edge. What a marmot paradise it must have been in those days.

Even now, several decades after the arrival of humans, Green Mountain's slopes remain thick with marmot families, as dense as the lush meadows will allow. We are neighbors, lookout and marmots, living our summers in open view of one another, though never going so far as to lend or borrow a cup of sugar. The marmot families that live nearest the lookout always keep a few yards between us. But they don't allow me to interrupt their grazing. By now the lookout's been part of their environment for generations. They clatter about in the wire fencing stored beneath the cabin and sometimes stroll along the wooden catwalk. I've even known one bold old codger to enter the open door and chew the battered linoleum that covers the wooden floor, while I sat there startled.

The hoary marmot is a rodent of the squirrel family, Sciuridae. It doesn't seem much like its relatives that share my yard, the chipmunks and ground squirrels. But it is quite similar to other members of the genus *Marmota,* such as the eastern woodchuck. It has two large incisors, seemingly more suitable for beaverlike logging practices than for merely snipping plants. Nonetheless, the marmot uses its formidable teeth only for clipping flowers and grasses. It doesn't brush between meals; its yellowed enamel and rude halitosis attest to that. But it sometimes grinds its incisors against rocks to keep them the right shape and size.

The marmot lives in burrows dug out between boulders. The ice-cleaved rock fin that forms the foundation of my home is so honeycombed with marmot passageways that I fear the boulders may someday part asunder and send the building over the edge of the cliff. The marmot spends most of its life in these underground chambers. For nine months of the year it hibernates, temperature lowered to nearly freezing, pulse slow, respiration on the brink of nonexistence. It is in these dens that the young are born and then remain for a cozy month or two before venturing into the world of light. In these dens the beast seeks shelter each night, and in daylight hours, too, should it spot predators on the prowl. The world aboveground mostly serves the marmot for two basic purposes: sunning and eating.

A hiker climbing the Green Mountain trail hears the marmots long before seeing one. A series of loud whistles accompanies the slow uphill tramp. The whistle always seems to be just ahead, repeating itself up the slope in ricocheted echoes, as if a Boy Scout troop were playing hide-and-seek behind the rocks and scattered trees. It is because of its unmistakable warning call that the marmot has been dubbed the "whistlepig." Yet the creature doesn't really whistle. It merely juts its tiny jaw and emits a long, shrill scream.

This whistle, the most popular word in the marmot vocabulary, means "Beware—stranger in sight." A fellow marmot browsing within earshot lifts its head to listen. If the whistles persist close by, the beast races through grasses and slides down snowbanks to the safety of the nearest den. At the burrow's mouth it stops, eyes, ears, and nose at attention. It may even sit up on its haunches, paws in the air, resting back to catch a better view, as does that other squirrel cousin, the prairie dog. Once it spots the source of alarm, it may begin to whistle as well. If the danger approaches too closely, however, the creature grows silent. It drops on all fours, eyes still strained outward, while its body sidles closer to the hole, legs tensed for a last-minute headfirst plunge into dark security.

Some people believe marmots post special sentinels on ridge outcroppings to keep an eye open for trouble. But I doubt they've evolved any regimented security system. The protruding rocks just happen to make good den sites, thus the population is densest near ridgetops. Since the stone slabs hold heat in this chilly upland, it's understandable that marmots should like to sprawl on them, limbs stretched wide, chin on the stone, dozing in the sun. This is the animal's favorite pose in early summer, when boulders have just begun to emerge from the sweeping drifts. If there's no rock handy, the marmots may sprawl spread-eagle on snowdrifts, like overheated dogs cooling their bellies.

The marmot's predilection for pinnacle perching provides a fire lookout like me an excellent early-warning system. There's no need for me to watch for approaching visitors. A good half hour before hikers pop into my yard, marmot whistles tell me guests are on their way. Or they're telling me that some unusual animal is crossing the meadow. By their ricocheting chain of shrieks, they even tell me the direction the interloper's traveling.

Marmot elders are my best informants. Fat and surly, they commandeer the finest rocks, chasing off any curious youngster who wanders close in hopes of a view. But whenever that larger, more ominous human beast wants to rest on their boulders, the elders quickly surrender their thrones. It's a pity, however, that the whistlepig hasn't learned basic hygiene. For the rocks on which he, as well as hikers, love to bask are littered with pungent black thumb-sized scat.

The hoary is the largest of the North American marmots, as much as double the weight of the eastern woodchuck. Because of its size, the whistlepig is worried by fewer predators than other members of the squirrel family. I have yet to see Mr. Coyote make off with one during his regular prowls on the slopes. Nor have I ever found the remains of a victim marmot on my own evening prowls through the meadows. Only once, on a still morning when fog hovered over the hardened snow, did a frantic series of whistles climax in a true marmot scream. A swift episode of invisible violence. Two or three panicky shrieks, followed immediately by half a whimper. Then all was foggy silence once more.

Though some predators may avoid the vicinity of the lookout on account of my presence, Green Mountain's healthy marmot population isn't due to my protectorship. The whistlepig can fend well enough for itself. I can attest to it. I once saw a marsh hawk swoop down on a large marmot. The hoary, instead of ducking and fleeing, pounced after the bird. The audacity of the hawk to skim so low over whistlepig grazing territory! As the marmot nipped at it, the hawk spun about in a flutter of alarm. Spread-winged, it sped out of sight, with the marmot chasing it downslope the whole while.

The hoary certainly has an ornery streak—brutishness so sullen that it seems more human than bestial. It doesn't stroll or trot along the trails it has worn into the mountainside, it skulks. It crawls low, eyes black with mistrust, a mistrust aimed especially toward its fellow marmots. Fighting is common among the clan, mostly just after the early-summer emergence. Sniffs of greeting between two whistlepigs turn into scrambled chases across snow mounds, down cliffs, along threatening precipices; bits of stone clatter down crevices and rattle onto snowfields.

A typical encounter I observed one day in the lookout's narrow front yard went like this: A curious yearling approached a marmot of it own size. The two beasts sniffed one another apprehensively fore and aft. They made a few tentative feints and retreats, then paused a moment. In a flash, they were at each other's throats, snapping and growling, tails lifted like angry skunks. Suddenly they grappled jaws. They grunted, tugged, and then rolled, twisted, tumbled downhill, their mouths locked. After a few minutes, their jaws parted. Mouths trembled, teeth chattered. The defender leapt forward, ready for another round. But the trespasser fell backward, half from clumsiness, half from fear, and retreated. Triumphant, the guardian struck a heroic pose, his bristly dun tail raised high.

At first such battles had me perplexed. I toyed with the idea that population pressures caused them. Then one day I had my eye on one ugly bloke who had hunks of back fur missing. He was bullying another hoary whom he had trapped between some rocks. From the ferocity of the attack, I was expecting murder, but his victim somehow escaped. Rabies, I mused with alarm; I even planned to carry a steel rod for protection whenever I ventured out of the building. But the beasts weren't foaming at the mouth, nor was their behavior otherwise peculiar. Perhaps marmots were merely passionate lovers—hence the big one's clawed back.

A bit of reading about the eastern woodchuck gave no single explanation for the tussles but hinted at a multiplicity of functions. They could be ritual greetings, exchanges of territorial information. Or a young male, testes swollen with ardor, may be flirting with a coy female. Or a weary mama may be chasing away a presumptuous, insinuating male with all the vengeful impatience of a dyed-in-wool feminist. What I do know, beyond all my conjecture, is that I've never seen a marmot fight draw blood.

In time I came to realize that the large bully marmot with the mangy back that sunned itself outside my door wasn't suffering from war wounds but was merely shedding its winter coat. And as summer progressed, the frequency and intensity of whistlepig battles abated until they finally came to an end.

There's one more marmot eccentricity I'd like to mention. It's an unusual intimacy that the hoaries and I share in nutritional matters. I'm not talking about one old codger who liked human food. He used to do well begging from hikers who lunched in my front yard. But when he realized that I wouldn't feed him, he gradually lost interest in human contact. No, I'm speaking about my urine, which is a favorite item because of its salts.

In early morning I see as many as seven hoaries on my favorite boulder. A few have even stayed in place while I wandered over to take my morning relief. There have even been times when the beasts squabbled underfoot, chasing off rivals while I bleary-eyed attempted to empty my bladder.

This curious behavior ends, however, as summer progresses. More meadow appears from beneath the snow, and the whistlepigs move farther afield. There's less opportunity to study their idiosyncrasies. Perhaps hikers' dogs have frightened them off. But it's more likely that the widening green pastures have enticed them away. Only one or two families stay close at hand. One stubborn elder holds sway on his favorite sunning rock not far down the ridge. Otherwise the marmots have settled for the role of distant sentries, posted afar in summer's rolling meadow.

Fire Lookout: Numa Ridge

Edward Abbey

July 12

We've been here ten days before I overcome initial inertia sufficient to begin this record. And keeping a record is one of the things the Park Service is paying us to do up here. The other, of course, is to keep our eyeballs peeled, alert for smoke. We are being paid a generous wage (about $3.25 an hour) to stay awake for at least eight hours a day. Some people might think that sounds like a pretty easy job. And they're right, it is an easy job, for some people. But not for all. When I mentioned to one young fellow down at park headquarters, a couple of weeks ago, that I was spending the summer on this fire lookout he shuddered with horror. "I'd go nuts in a place like that," he said, thinking of solitary confinement. I didn't tell him I was cheating, taking my wife along. But that can be risky too; many a good marriage has been shattered on the rock of isolation.

Renée and I walked up here on July 2, packs on our backs, two hours ahead of the packer with his string of mules. The mules carried the heavier gear, such as our bedrolls, enough food and water for the first two weeks, seven volumes of Marcel Proust, and Robert Burton's *Anatomy of Melancholy.* Light summer reading. Renée had never worked a fire lookout before, but I had, and I knew that if I was ever going to get through the classics of world lit it could only be on a mountain top, far above the trashy plains of *Rolling Stone, Playboy,* the *New York Times,* and *Mizz* magazine.

The trail is about six miles long from Bowman Lake and climbs 3,000 feet. We made good time, much better time than we wished because we were hustled along, all the way, by hordes of bloodthirsty mosquitoes. We had prepared ourselves, of course, with a heavy treatment of government-issue insect repellent on our faces, necks, arms, but that did not prevent the mosquitoes from whining in our ears and hovering close to eye, nostril, and mouth.

We also had the grizzly on our mind. Fresh bear scat on the trail, unpleasant crashing noises back in the dark of the woods and brush, reminded us that we were intruding, uninvited, into the territory of *Ursus horribilis,* known locally as G-bear or simply (always in caps) as GRIZ. It was in Glacier, of course, only a few years ago, that two young women had been killed on the same night by grizzlies. We clattered our tin cups now and then, as advised, to warn the bears we were coming. I was naturally eager to see a GRIZ in the wild, something I'd never done, but not while climbing up a mountain with a pack on my back, tired, sweaty, and bedeviled by bugs. Such an encounter, in such condition, could only mean a good-natured surrender on my part; I wasn't *about* to climb a tree.

Bear stories. My friend Doug Peacock was soaking one time in a hot spring in Yellowstone's back country. Surprised by a grizzly sow and her two cubs, he scrambled naked as a newt up the nearest pine; the bear kept him there, freezing in the breeze, for two hours. Another: Riley McClelland, former park naturalist at Glacier, and a friend were treed by a GRIZ. Remembering that he had an opened sardine can in his pack, Riley watched with sinking heart as the bear sniffed at it. Disdaining the sardine lure, however, the bear tore up the other man's pack to get at a pair of old tennis shoes.

Sacrifice, that may be the key to coexistence with the GRIZ. If we surprise one on the trail, I'll offer up first my sweat-soaked hat. If that won't do, then cheese and salami out of the pack. And if that's not enough, well, then nothing else to do, I guess, but push my wife his way. *Droit du seigneur à la montagne,* etc.

We reach the lookout without fulfilling any fantasies. The lookout is a two-room, two-story wood frame cabin at timberline, 7,000 feet above sea level. On the north, east, and southeast stand great peaks— Reuter, Kintla, Numa, Chapman, Rainbow, Vulture. Northwest we can see a bit of the Canadian Rockies. West and southwest lie the North Fork of the Flathead River, a vast expanse of Flathead National Forest, and on the horizon the Whitefish Range. Nice view: 360 degrees of snow-capped scenic splendor, lakes, forest, river, fearsome peaks, and sheltering sky.

We remove the wooden shutters from the lookout windows, shovel snow from the stairway, unlock the doors. The pack string arrives. The

packer and I unload the mules, the packer departs, Renée and I unpack
our goods and move in. Except for a golden-mantled ground squirrel
watching us from the rocks, a few Clark's nutcrackers in the subalpine
firs, we seem to be absolutely alone.

July 14 (Bastille Day!)

The Great Revolution was a failure, they say. All revolutions have been
failures, they say. To which I reply: All the more reason to make
another one. Knocking off "work" at five o'clock (the transition from
work to nonwork being here discernible by a subtle reshading in the
colors of the rock on Rainbow Peak), my wife and I honor this day by
uncorking a bottle of genuine Beaujolais. With Renée's home-baked
crusty French bread and some real longhorn cheese from the country
store down at the hamlet of Polebridge, it makes a fitting celebration.

A golden eagle soars by *below us,* pursued by—a sparrow hawk? My
wife the bird-watcher is uncertain; but it must have been. Looking
unhurried but pursuing a straight course, the eagle disappears into the
vast glacial cirque above Okokala Lake, followed steadily, slightly above,
by the smaller bird. More Clark's nutcrackers. Chipping sparrows.
Mountain chickadees. Oregon juncoes. Clouds of mosquitoes whining
at the windows, greedy for blood. A doe, a fawn, a yearling buck with
velvet horns jostling one another at our salt deposits on the rocks outside. The doe is dominant; the young buck retreats. Women's Lib has
reached out even here, for God's sake, all the way from Washington
Square to Numa Ridge. Depressing thought. Striving to uphold the
natural superiority of the male, I have beaten my wife—at chess—five
games straight. Now she refuses to play with me. You can't win.

What *do* people do on a lookout tower when, as now, the season is
wet and there are no fires? Aside from the obvious, and reading Proust
and *The Anatomy of Melancholy,* we spend hours just gazing at the world
through binoculars. For example, I enjoy climbing the local mountains,
scaling the most hideous bare rock pitches step by step, hand by hand,
without aids, without rope or partners, clinging to fragments of loose
shale, a clump of bear grass, the edge of an overhanging snow cornice,
above a nightmarish abyss, picking a route toward even higher and
more precarious perches—through these U.S. Navy 7×50 lenses. The
effortless, angelic, and supine approach to danger.

It's not all dreaming. There are some daily chores. Ever since arrival
I've been packing snow to the lookout from a big drift a hundred yards
below, carrying it up in buckets, dumping it into steel garbage cans, let-

ting it melt in the sun. Now we've got 120 gallons of snow water in addition to the drinking water brought up by muleback. Then there's firewood. Although we have a propane stove for cooking, the only heat in the lookout comes from an old cast-iron cookstove. And with the kind of rainy, windy weather we've been having, heat is a necessity. Even in July. So a couple of times a week I go down the trail with ax and saw, fell one of many dead trees in the area—fir, whitebark pine—buck the log into eighteen-inch lengths, tote it up the hill armload by armload.

Three times a day we take weather observations—wind speed and direction, temperature, relative humidity—or my wife does, since she is the scientist in this family. We wash windows, occasionally. We patch and repair things. We listen to the Park Service radio and the Forest Service radio, ready to relay messages if necessary. I entertain the deer and the squirrels with my flute. Renée bakes things, studies the maps, memorizes the terrain. But mostly we sit quietly out on the catwalk, reading about aristocratic life in *fin-de-siècle* Paris and looking at northwestern Montana in the summer of '75.

This is a remote place indeed, far from the center of the world, far away from all that's going on. Or is it? Who says so? Wherever two human beings are alive, together, and happy, there is the center of the world. You out there, brother, sister, you too live in the center of the world, no matter where or what you think you are.

July 16

Heavy cloud buildup in northwest. Lightning likely, fire danger rising, humidity dropping. The haze lies heavy over yonder Whitefish Range, obscuring the farther peaks. Looks like smog, but is only water vapor, dust, the smoke from many campfires along the North Fork. They tell us.

One longs for a nice little forest fire. We need some excitement around this joint. Nothing healthier for the forests than a good brisk fire now and then to clear out the undergrowth, give the moose and bear some living room. Besides we need the overtime pay. If that idiot Smokey the Bear (the noted ursine bore) had *his* way all us fire fighters would starve to death.

We see a Townsend's solitaire, abundant here. Hermit thrush. Swallowtail butterflies. Little spiders hanging on threads from the attic trapdoor. A six-legged spider (war veteran) on the outside of the windowpane chewing on a mosquito. Good show! mate. One snowshoe hare loping into the brush.

Gordon the Garbage Man, one of the park's seasonal employees, comes up the mountain for a visit, leaves us two big Dolly Vardens fresh from the lake. Fried by my frau, filleted and anointed with lemon, they make a delicately delicious supper. If I weren't so corrupt and lazy, I'd take hook and line myself, drop down to Lake Okokala 1,200 feet below, and catch a similar supper every evening. According to the old logbooks here, at least some of the previous lookouts used to do that.

Officially, all measurements at Glacier National Park are now given in meters. All road and trail signs, all park maps, show distances and heights in meters and kilometers, without their Anglo-American equivalents. The Park Service, no doubt at the instigation of the Commerce Department, is trying to jam the metric system down our throats whether we want it or not. We can be sure this is merely the foot in the door, the bare beginning of a concerted effort by Big Business–Big Government (the two being largely the same these days) to force the metric system upon the American people. Why? Obviously for the convenience of world trade, technicians, and technology, to impose on the entire planet a common system of order. All men must march to the beat of the same drum, like it or not.

July 17
Still no real fires, aside from a few trivial lightning-storm flare-ups in the forest across the river, soon drowned by rain. But we are ready. Perhaps I should describe the equipment and operations of a lookout.

We live and work in the second story of the cabin. The ground-floor room, dark and dank, is used only for storage. Our room is light, airy, and bright, with windows running the length of all four walls. Closable louvered vents above each window admit fresh air while keeping out rain. In the center of this twelve-foot by twelve-foot room, oriented squarely with the four directions, stands the chest-high fire finder. The Osborne Fire Finder consists essentially of a rotating metal ring about two feet in diameter with a handle to turn it by and a pair of sights, analogous to the front and rear sights of a rifle, mounted upright on opposite sides. When the lookouts spots a fire, he aims this device at the base and center of the smoke (or flame, if discovered at night) and obtains an azimuth reading from the fixed base of the fire finder, which is marked off into 360 degrees. By use of the vernier scale attached to the rotating ring, the lookout can get a reading not only in degrees but precisely to the nearest minute, or one-sixtieth of a degree.

Having determined the compass direction of the fire from his own location, the lookout must still establish the location of the fire. To do that he must be able to recognize and identify the place where the fire is burning and to report its distance from his lookout station. A metal tape stretched between front and rear sights of the fire finder, across a circular map inside the rotating ring, gives the distance in kilometers. Another aid is the sliding peep sight on the rear sight, by means of which the lookout can obtain a vertical angle on his fire. Through a bit of basic trigonometry the vertical angle can be translated into distance. Or if another lookout, at a different station, can see the same fire, the line of his azimuth reading extended across a map of the area intersects the line of the first lookout's reading to give the exact point of the fire. Assuming both lookouts are awake, fairly competent, and on duty at the same time.

If these procedures sound complicated, that is an illusion. The technical aspects of a lookout's job can be mastered by any literate anthropoid with an IQ of not less than seventy in about two hours. It's the attitude that's difficult: Unless you have an indolent, melancholy nature, as I do, you will not be happy as an official United States government fire lookout.

Anyway, having determined the location of his fire, and being reasonably certain it is a fire and not a smoking garbage dump, a controlled slash burn, a busy campground, floating vapors, or traffic dust rising from a dirt road, the lookout picks up his radio microphone or telephone and reports his discovery to fire-control headquarters. After that his main task becomes one of assisting the smoke-chasers in finding the fire, relaying messages, looking for new and better fires.

July 20

Bear claw scratches on the wooden walls of the ground-floor storage room. Last thing before retiring each night I set the bear barrier in place on the stairway leading to our quarters. The bear barrier is a wooden panel with many nails driven through it, points all sticking out. Supposed to discourage *Ursus stairiensis* from climbing up to our catwalk balcony. In a previous lookout's log we had read this entry:

> Woke up this morning to see a big black bear staring at me thru window, about six inches from my face. Chased him off with a Pulaski.

The Pulaski is a fire-fighting tool, a combination ax and pickax. I keep one handy too, right under the bed where I can reach it easy. I'd keep it under the pillow if my old lady would let me.

Thinking about GRIZ. Almost every day, on the park or forest radio, we hear some ranger report a bear sighting, sometimes of grizzly. Campers molested, packs destroyed by hungry and questing bears. Somebody was recently attacked and mauled by a GRIZ north of the line, in Waterton Lakes. Bear jams on the park highway, though not so common here as they used to be in Yellowstone, before so many of Yellowstone's bears mysteriously disappeared, do occur in Glacier from time to time.

No doubt about it, the presence of bear, especially grizzly bear, adds a spicy titillation to a stroll in the woods. My bear-loving friend Peacock goes so far as to define wilderness as a place and only a place where one enjoys the opportunity of being attacked by a dangerous wild animal. Any place that lacks GRIZ, or lions or tigers, or a rhino or two, is not, in his opinion, worthy of the name "wilderness." A good definition, worthy of serious consideration. A wild place without dangers is an absurdity, although I realize that danger creates administrative problems for park and forest managers. But we must not allow our national parks and national forests to be degraded to the status of mere public playgrounds. Open to all, yes of course. But—*enter at your own risk.*

Enter Glacier National Park and you enter the homeland of the grizzly bear. We are uninvited guests here, intruders, the bear our reluctant host. If he chooses, now and then, to chase somebody up a tree, or all the way to the hospital, that is the bear's prerogative. Those who prefer, quite reasonably, not to take such chances should stick to Disneyland in all its many forms and guises.

July 22

Bowman Lake 3,000 feet below looks more like clear Pennzoil than water. A milky turquoise green color, strange to my eyes. The North Fork even more so. The cause is not man-made pollution of any sort, but what is called "glacier milk," a solution of powdered rock washed down from under the bellies of the glaciers hanging all around us under the high peaks.

Toy boats glide up and down the lake, trailing languorous wakes that spread across the oil-smooth water in slow-subsiding ripples. Anglers at work. The fishing is poor this summer, they say; weather too wet, too much insect life in the air and floating down the streams.

Too wet? You can say that again. This is the foggiest, boggiest, buggiest country I have ever seen in my life. Everywhere I look, below timberline, the land is clothed in solid unbroken greenery. Damp, humid green all over the place—gives the country an unhealthy look. I guess I really am a desert rat. The sound of all these verdant leafy things breathing and sweating and photosynthesizing around me all the time makes me nervous. Trees, I believe (in the ardor of my prejudice), like men, should be well spaced off from one another, not more than one to a square mile. Space and scarcity give us dignity. And liberty. And thereby beauty.

Oyster stew for lunch. Out of tin can. Had buckwheat cakes for breakfast, with wild huckleberry syrup by Eva Gates, Bigfork, Montana.

Enormous clouds with evil black bottoms floating in from the Pacific, great sailing cities of cumulo-nimbus. Lightning plays among their massy depths. Will it bring us fire? God, one hopes so. What are we up here for, perched like condors on this mighty mountain, if not to conjure up a storm? The children need shoes. All those fire fighters down at headquarters need overtime. The forest needs a rebirth, a renascence, a weeding out.

July 23

Down the mountain I go, returning same day with mail, wine, cheese, other essentials. I sing, as I march along, songs I hope will warn the GRIZ of my approach. But what kind of music does the GRIZ like? Suppose he hates old cowboy songs? Or Puccini?

All the way up the mountain, under a dark and grumbling sky, a personal cloud of hungry mosquitoes envelopes my head. I am relieved and glad when the first lightning strikes begin to bounce off the crags above. Am less glad when I reach the open ridge at timberline with jagged high-voltage bolts crashing all around. No place to hide now; I keep going for the relative safety of the lookout cabin and reach it just as the storm bursts out in all its awful grandeur.

We cower inside in the dark, Renée and I, trying to stay away from all metal objects, as instructed. But, of course, the lookout is crowded with metallic objects—iron stoves, fire finder, steel cots, water cans, buckets, ax, dishpan. We can feel the next charge building up; we stand on the negative terminal of a high-powered electrical system, the positive pole directly overhead. Our skin prickles, our hair stands up. We hear a fizzing noise above us, on the roof of the cabin where the lightning rod sticks up. A crackling sound, like a burning fuse. I know what's coming now, and an instant later it comes, a flash that fills the room with blue-white light, accompanied simultaneously by a jarring crash, as if the entire cabin had been dropped from the sky upon our rocky ridge. No harm done. The building is thoroughly grounded, top and sides, and Thor's hammer blow passes on safely into the heart of the mountain. Lightning strikes many times in the same place. As every lookout learns.

That evening we spot a couple of small flare-ups across the river in the national forest. But both are soon drowned out by rain and never go anywhere.

July 27

The bird list grows slowly. Add barn swallow, cliff swallow, water pipit, raven, blue grouse, white-tailed ptarmigan, rufous hummingbird, brown creeper, gray jay, evening grosbeak, red-shafted flicker, loon. *Loon!*—heard from the lake far below—that wild, lorn, romantic cry, one of the most thrilling sounds in all North America. Sound of the ancient wilderness, lakes, forest, moonlight, birchbark canoes.

We have also seen two cow moose, one with calf, romping through the fields below the lookout, and a badger, several black bear (but no GRIZ yet), elk droppings, mountain goat tracks, least chipmunks, ground squirrels, pikas, hoary marmots, many deer. And there's a big wood rat living downstairs among the water cans, firewood, tools, and boxes. Met him the other day.

The flowers have been blooming, on and off, ever since we got here. We've identified the following so far: purple-eyed mariposa, false asphodel, valerium, harebell, blue penstemon, arnica, fleabane, mountain penstemon, bear grass, sulfur flower, stonecrop, Indian paintbrush, alum root, glacier lily, prince's pine, mountain gentian, forget-me-not, bluebonnet, alpine buttercup, yellow columbine, elephant head, blanket flower, alpine aster, swamp laurel, fireweed.

The bear grass, with its showy panicle of flowers on a two- or three-foot stalk, is the most striking flower in Glacier. It reminds me of pictures of the giant lobelia on the slopes of Mount Kilimanjaro. The deer eat the flower stalks.

Bear sighting reported on park radio: A ranger reports one grizzly sow with two cubs in "Moose Country," along the Going-to-the-Sun Highway. The bear, he says, is reared up on her hind legs, roaring and waving her arms at tourists as they surround her, their cameras clicking. He breaks it up. Nobody hurt. This time.

The park radio is our chief amusement. Over a million people visited the park last summer, most of them driving through by way of the Going-to-the-Sun. Many traffic problems every day, much police work.

Exempli gratia 1: 1961 converted schoolbus at Logan Pass, brakes burned out, driver thinks he can bring bus down mountain by driving in low gear, requests ranger escort. Not allowed. Tow truck dispatched.

E.g. 2: Ranger reports distraught wife and children at Lake McDonald campground. "Woman is very upset," he says. Cause? Her husband, the children's father, went off on a hike with a fifteen-year-old baby-sitter, been gone for hours. (Family is reunited later in evening.)

E.g. 3: Rookie ranger reports five bikers camping under highway bridge and smoking a controlled substance. "I think they're smoking dope," he says, "although, of course, I don't know what dope smells like."

Our friend Gus Chambers up on Swiftcurrent Lookout in the center of the park spots the first genuine park fire of the season. (And the only one, as it turns out.) He gives his azimuth reading, the UTM (Universal Transverse Mercator) coordinates, locates it one kilometer south-southeast of Redhorn Lake. No one can see the fire but Gus; we other lookouts are sick with envy and rage. One snag burning in a small valley, remote from any trail; too windy for smoke jumpers, fire fighters are flown to scene by helicopter.

Fire caused by lightning. When Smokey Bear says that only *You* can prevent forest fires, Smokey is speaking an untruth. A falsehood. Ninety percent of the fires in the American West are lightning-caused, as they have been for the last 20,000 years, or ever since the glaciers retreated. Yet the forests survived. And thrived. Hard to explain this to some old-time foresters, who often feel the same passionate hatred for fire that sheepmen feel for coyotes. Now, after fifty years of arduous fire-suppression effort, the useful role of natural fire in the forest ecosystem is becoming recognized among foresters. But the public, indoctrinated for so long in the Smokey Bear ethic, may not be easy to reeducate.

No one disputes the fact that it will always be necessary to quell forest fires that threaten lives, homes, business establishments, or valuable stands of timber scheduled for logging.

July 30

Renée bakes a prune pie. An experiment. I read Burton on "Heroical Love." The days sail by with alarming speed; why this headlong descent into *oblivion?* What's the rush? Sinking comfortably into the sloth and decay of my middle middle age, I am brought up short nevertheless, now and then, by the alarming realization that all men, so far, have proved mortal. Me too? Each day seems more beautiful than the last. Every moment becomes precious. Thus are we driven to the solitary pleasures of philosophy, the furtive consolations of thought.

Gus's fire is out. Burnt only five acres. Snow slides in Logan Pass again, traffic halted. Hiker killed on Snyder Lake trail, trying to climb cliff. Child lost and found. Woman, sixty-seven, lost for three hours near Bowman Lake. Found. GRIZ trees three hikers at Trout Lake.

More bugs. Mosquitoes as numerous as ever, soon to be augmented by swarms of flying ants. And now another enemy, the moose fly, appears, the bloodsucking *Muscas horribilis sangria*. Mean, vicious Draculas with wings. About the size of bats. We stay inside when the wind dies and all these flying plagues come forth together.

I read the old lookout logs. First of all Numa Ridge lookouts was Scotty Beaton, who worked here twenty-two summers, beginning in 1928. Unlike all succeeding lookouts, whose logbook entries tend (like mine) to rant and ramble, Scotty kept his notations terse, laconic, to the point. Viz.:

> *Aug. 2, 1945:* Hot & dry done my usual chores
> *July 28, 1946:* Very warm—Hugh Buchanan the ranger came up with a Paper to have me Pledge I wouldn't overthrow the government that never entered my mind in the fifty five years I been in this country
> *July 5, 1948:* Moved up today the bears had moved into the lower part of the Lookout & took a few bites out of the upper story. The lower part a hell of a mess.
> *July 22, 1949:* Done usual chores
> *Sept. 11, 1950:* Found mud in bottom of water barrel put there by youngster from McFarland's dude ranch. Same kid who broke crosshairs on firefinder, tramped down nails in bear board and set my binoculars on the hot stove.

According to the logbooks, every lookout since Scotty found Numa Ridge a delightful place—but only one of the twenty-four (including many couples) came back for a second season, and the second was enough for him. In the fire lookout's vocation many are called, few chosen. The isolation is too much for most. This is my seventh summer as a lookout; I guess I like it.

Down on Loneman Peak in the southern part of Glacier sits

Leonard Stittman. This is his fourteenth summer on Loneman. In all those summers he has had a total of eight visitors, all of them rangers.

We've had a ranger-visitor too—Art Sedlack, the man who shot the snowmobile.

It happened one night in December 1974. Sedlack, on duty at Walton Ranger Station in Glacier, caught a snowmobiler buzzing around in an area where snowmobiles are not supposed to be. This sort of thing had been going on for a long time, and the operator of this particular snowmobile was a repeat offender. Suddenly inspired, Sedlack drew his trusty .38 Ranger Special and shot the snowmobile right through the head. "One snowmobile, immobilized," he reported by radio. Sensation! For a while Sedlack's rear end was in a sling as the owner of the slain snowmobile and other local motorized recreationists demanded blood, a head for a head. Sedlack might have lost his job but for an outpouring of public support, phone calls and letters from all over western Montana. Reconsidering, the park administration suspended him for one week without pay, then sent him to the service's police-training school in Washington, D.C. Now he is back in Glacier, an unrepentant and even better ranger.

Art talks about the bear problem in the national parks. Really a human problem. Too many humans crowding the roads and trails, conflict inevitable. Solution: Reduce population. Which population? Ah yes, indeed, that is the question.

A bear, when caught in mischief, is tranquilized and tagged on the ear. Caught again, it is tagged on the other ear. A bear with both ears tagged is in trouble. It may be transported to a locality remote from human activity, but this is not a solution. There are no vacant areas in nature. The newcomer bear is not welcome among established inhabitants, is harried, fought, driven out by native bears, becomes a loner, an outlaw, a rogue—doomed. If caught in trouble a third time he or she will likely be "taken away" for good. That is, shot dead.

August 2

Fog and rain. Foul is fair and fair is foul. Cut more wood, keeping bin full. When I go down the hill to the john in the morning I find the mosquitoes huddled inside, waiting for me as usual. As usual I light up a Roi-Tan, a good cheap workingman's cigar, and the mosquitoes flee, choking and swearing. I sit there and contemplate, through the smoke, the dim shapes of fir tree and mule deer through the mists. On clear mornings, sunshine on my lap, I can look right down on the pearly, oily, iridescent surface of Bowman Lake in all its incredible rich blueness. I think, if I think at all, about simplicity, convenience, the advantages of what I call Positive Poverty.

There is of course no flush toilet on a fire lookout. But the pit toilet is a perfectly adequate, comfortable and even pleasant substitute for the elaborate bathrooms of the modern home. A little lime or wood ashes keep down the odors, discourage flies. In cold weather one kerosene or Coleman lamp keeps the outhouse warm enough. What more does one need? And no freezing pipes, no water pump, no septic tank to worry about, no awful plumber's bills. And the basic good sense of it: Instead of flushing our bodily wastes into the public water supply, we plant them back in the good earth where they belong. Where our bodies must go as well, in due course, if we are to keep the good earth productive.

Nor is there running water up here. Or electricity. I carry the water by the bucketful up from the barrels in the cellar. We heat the water on the wood stove, wash and scald-rinse the dishes in a pair of dishpans, bathe (when we feel like it) in a small galvanized tub set on the floor or out on the catwalk when the sun is shining. Before the big drifts melted, Renée and I sometimes scrubbed ourselves with handfuls of snow, standing naked on the dazzling snowbanks, in the heat of the sun.

Hauling water, cutting firewood, using a pit toilet seem like only normalcy to me, raised as I was on a backwoods Pennsylvania farm. For Renée, a city girl, these methods are new, but she adapts at once, without difficulty, to such minor deprivations. No problem at all. Most of what we call modern conveniences are no more than that at best. They are far from being necessities. And what a terrible price most of us have to pay for our tract homes, our fancy plumbing, our automobiles, our "labor-saving" appliances, the luxuriously packaged ersatz food in the supermarkets, all that mountain of metal junk and plastic garbage under which our lives are smothered. Men *and* women trapped in the drudgery and tedium of meaningless jobs (see Studs Terkel's *Working* if you don't believe me), and the despoliation of a continent, the gray skies, the ruined rivers, the ravaged hills, the clearcut forests, the industrialized farms, all to keep that Gross National Product growing ever grosser. Madness and folly. Untouched by human hands. Unguided by human minds.

Not that technology and industrialism are evil in themselves. The problem is to get them down to human scale, to keep them under human control, to prevent them from ever again becoming the self-perpetuating, ever-expanding monsters we have allowed them to become. What we need is an optimum industrialism, neither too much nor too little, a truly sophisticated, unobtrusive, below-ground technology. For certainly science, technology, industrialism have given us a number of good things. Not many, but some. My list begins with the steel ax. Matches. Nails, hammer, handsaw. Writing paper and pen and ink. The birth-control pill. Or the condom. (Forget-me-not.) Galvanized bucket—no, strike that item; the old oaken bucket is good enough. The cast-iron stove. Electricity. And solar heating. Windmills and suction pumps. Candles, Aladdin lamps, pianos, and platinum flutes. The coal-burning locomotive, transcontinental train service, the horse collar, the pneumatic-tired wagon, bicycles, the rocket-powered spaceship. But not automobiles. (What? Spaceships! Yes. Why not? I believe space exploration is a worthy human adventure.) Radios and record players, but not television. Anesthetics and aspirin, but not BHT, sodium nitrite, monosodium glutamate, or artificial coloring. The democratic rifle and the egalitarian revolver, but not the authoritarian B-52. And so on.

But we cannot pick and choose this way, some technophiles may insist—it's the entire package, plagues and all, or nothing. To which one must reply: If that is true then we have indeed lost control and had better dismantle the whole structure. But it is not true: We *can* pick and choose, we can learn to select this and reject that. Discrimination is a basic function of the human intelligence. Are we to be masters or slaves of the techno-industrial machine?

My cigar has gone out. The mosquitoes come sneaking back. They whine around my ears like the sirens of commerce, like bill collectors, like the National Association of Manufacturers. The sound of greed.

Time to sharpen the old ax. A chill wind is blowing and the fog rolls in again. Dark birds flap through the mist, croaking for blood.

August 3
Done usual lookout chores.

August 4
Done usual lookout chores. To wit: woke, ate, answered radio check, looked, chopped wood, carried water, read Burton ("Of all causes of this affliction," he writes, meaning romantic love, "the most remote are the stars"), looked, releveled fire finder, washed dishes, played chess then flute, watched sun go down, went to bed.

In the evening after sundown an owl flies round and round the lookout, swooping silent as a moth through the fog and gloom, checking out our chipmunks. Barred owl? Short-eared owl? Hard to tell in this darkness. A spooky bird of ill import.

August 5
My wife looks prettier every day. By God, a man begins to get ideas in a place like this.

August 7
High winds all day, clear sky, scudding clouds. The surface of the lake below, stirred by the wind, looks like brushed aluminum, has the color of my knife blade. The peaks round about stand forth in startling, blazing, preternatural brilliance. A cold, immaculate clarity. Shall we climb Rainbow Peak one of these days? Ever see Goat Haunt? Belly River? Mount Despair? Loneman? Gunsight Pass? Rising Wolf Mountain? Spirit Lake? Two Medicine Mountain? Almost A Dog Mountain? Vulture Peak?

August 11
Storms. Fog and drizzle, brief blaze of sun—a rainbow floats in the fog below.

Lightning again, flashing through the mist; then thunder rumbles in at a thousand feet per second. Pink lightning. Heaven and earth link nerves in illuminated ecstasy—or is it pain? Once, in another place, I saw lightning score a direct hit on a juniper tree. The tree exploded in a burst of flame.

Now comes another direct hit on our lookout. First the buzzing sound, the eerie *hiss* and *fizz* directly overhead. That sinister touch, God's fingertip upon our roof. Light, deadly, an almost dainty touch, you might say. Followed by the flash of light and the *crack!* of a great whip. The building vibrates.

When the hard winds blow the cabin creaks and groans, tugging at the cables that keep it anchored to the rock. On our east side the ridge drops off at fifty degrees down a treeless slope to the bottom of the cirque 600 feet below.

In the evening things settle down a bit. We go for a walk down the trail, down through the drifting fog. The huckleberries are ripening now, but it looks like a poor crop. The bears will be roaming and irritable. Mushrooms bulge through the damp duff under the pines—fat, brown, speckled domes of fungoid flesh. Delicacies for the deer. The mushrooms remind me of bitter days at another lookout post, 2,000 miles away and a decade in the past. I was enduring the agonies of unrequited love, exactly as Burton describes them, and in my misery I contemplated with interest some of the mushrooms growing all about the tower of that other lookout; the rosy hoods of *Amanita muscaria* suggested the possibility of flight beyond the sorrows of this sublunar sphere. But I refrained, not from fear of hallucination or death, but because I was becoming accustomed to the realization that I enjoyed my sufferings more. So the girl I loved had betrayed me by running off with her husband. What of it? I survived.

Men have died and worms have eaten them, but not for love.

August 15

Been gone three days, leaving Renée to man the lookout on her own. She was willing and ready and is in fact a better fire lookout than I. Much more conscientious, not so corrupted by subversive notions of fire ecology, etc.

Down from Numa Ridge, the first thing I did was go to Logan Pass, hike the Highline Trail to Granite Park and up Swiftcurrent Peak to visit Gus at his fire lookout. Late in the evening I returned to Logan Pass. Nineteen miles round trip. On the way I had passed a group of mountain goats, six of them, grazing not fifty feet from the trail, indifferent to my presence. Returning at twilight, I encountered five bighorn rams bunched up right on the trail, blocking my way. They showed no inclination to move and I wasn't going to climb around them. I approached to within twenty feet, waved my arms and whistled; grudgingly they got up and let me through. That's the way it is in the Peaceable Kingdom, the wildlife so accustomed to hikers they won't even get out of your way.

I had timed my walk badly. The dark settled in while I was still five miles from Logan Pass, the road, and my car. The trail wound through thickets of alder brush, with a cliff on my left and a drop-off on my right. A cloudy, starless night. Hard to see more than ten, fifteen feet ahead. Odd noises off in the thickets. I began to think about GRIZ again. What to do if I met one now? No climbable trees in sight and my only weapon a pocketknife. Words of wisdom, often heard at Glacier, whispered through my brain: "Anyone who hikes alone, after dark, is asking for trouble." Bears are omnivorous, have no pride at all, will eat anything, even authors. Even if the GRIZ hears me coming, I realized, he will have difficulty getting out of my way on this mountain trail. We'd have to sidle past one another, smiling apologetically, like strangers in a narrow doorway. I walked on, singing loudly, feeling foolish, half amused by my own fear. Yes, I did want to meet a grizzly in the wild—but not just yet. Nothing happened that night. I saw nothing but shadows, heard nothing but the wind and those obscure crashing sounds, now and then, below the trail.

August 16

Old magazines on the shelves under the fire finder, left here by former lookouts. I leaf through *Field & Stream, Outdoor Life, Hook & Bullet News.* Here's an interesting item:

> *Stock taking.* California has a new procedure for scattering the trout it stocks in streams in an attempt to foil hatchery-truck chasers. The fish are not released until dusk or after dark and are placed in one spot rather than in several. Wardens report that the fish are well scattered by daylight and the night stocking stymies the truck followers.

And another:

> *Pump Priming.* In an effort to stimulate the lagging fishing and subsequent business decline caused by the ban on keeping fish caught in Lake St. Clair, the Michigan Marine and Snow-mobile Dealers Association is trying to raise $50,000 to $100,000 to finance the tagging of thousands of fish that would be worth anywhere from $100 to $10,000 apiece to the anglers catching them. The ban resulted from mercury contamination tests run on some of the Lake's fish.

So it goes, sportsmen.

Reflections on hunting. My father was a hunter. During the Great Depression and the war years, he killed dozens of deer, hundreds of cottontail rabbits, in order to put meat on the table for his hungry family. My mother would can the extra rabbit, putting it up in jars. During the fifties and sixties, as the times got better, my father gradually gave up hunting. Never in his life has he killed another living thing for sport. Except, that is, during his boyhood. Before he grew up. Hunters, he would explain, never kill for sport.

All those red-coated men we see out in the field during deer season—what are they up to? Well, some of them are hunters, engaged in the ancient, honorable, and serious business of providing meat for kith and kin. The majority, however, outnumbering the hunters and the deer as well by ninety-nine to one, are not hunters but merely gunners. Sportsmen.

The sportsman's pursuit of game is incidental to his primary purposes, which can be defined as follows, in descending order of importance:

1. Get away from wife and kids for a few days
2. Get drunk and play poker with cronies by the light of a Coleman lamp in tent, lodge, or Winnebago
3. Swap lies with same
4. Maybe shoot some legal game
5. Failing that, shoot some illegal game—cow, horse, chicken, game warden, etc.
6. Failing that, shoot *something*—side of barn, road sign, his own foot, whatever's handy

How do I know about this? Because I was there. I too was once a sportsman. But I grew up. In that one respect anyhow. Like my old man, Paul, who beat me to it.

August 18
Somebody falls into McDonald Falls again. "Bring the wagon," radios ranger. The hurry-up wagon. Happens every year. As at North Rim, Grand Canyon, where somebody disappears every summer.

Whole family mauled by a grizzly on Grinnel Glacier trail. Father, mother, two children. Apparently the children had been walking far ahead of their parents, got between a sow and her cub. Children attacked. Their screams bring father running to the scene, who attempts to fight off the GRIZ with his bare hands. Reinforced by mother, the bear knocks them both about, then wanders off. Entire family hospitalized with serious injuries. Rangers close trail to further hiking for time being.

Might be hard to explain to those people why the grizzly bear is a vital part of the Glacier wilderness. But it is. The parks are for people?

Certainly. And for bears also? Absolutely. How do we resolve the inevitable conflict? Are we going to ration the wilderness experience? Probably; that process has already begun at Glacier National Park, where back-country camping is restricted to certain sites, requiring written permits and advance reservations. A sad and ominous but unavoidable expedient.

One calamity after another. One mishap after another. A ranger's work is never done. And more and more, in every national park, that work consists largely of police work. The urbanization of our national parks. All through the summer bumper-to-bumper auto traffic crawls up and down the Going-to-the-Sun Highway. I've said it before and I'll say it again, we've got to close the parks to private cars if we want to keep them as parks. The parks are for people, not machines. Let the machines find their own parks. Most of America has been surrendered to them already, anyway. New Jersey, for example. Southern California.

On the forest radio, the weather report concludes as usual with the daily fire-fighting capability report: "We have available in Missoula today fifty-two smoke jumpers, two B-16s, one Neptune, two twin Beechcraft, two helicopters, four DC-7s, etc." All on standby, in readiness.

There used to be ten active fire-lookout stations in Glacier. Now there are only four. My old lookout tower on North Rim was deactivated five years ago. More and more lookouts are superseded by aircraft patrols. Part of the national industrializing pattern, human beings put out of work by machines. Labor-intensive jobs (so to speak) made obsolete by capital-intensive substitutes. One hour of an airplane's time costs more than two or three days' pay for a human lookout on a mountaintop. But no doubt it is, as they say, more efficient. And what happens to all the displaced fire lookouts? They swell the ranks of the unemployed. They wander the streets of small western towns, kicking beer cans around, getting in trouble.

Who cares? Most fire lookouts are crazy anyhow. Once from a peak in southern Arizona, at sundown, with the western sky full of smoke, dust, and clouds, I looked straight at the sun with my lookout's binoculars. I knew it was a foolish thing to do. Could have ruined my eyes forever. At the very least might have impaired my night vision. But the haze seemed so extremely dense, the sun so blood-red behind it, that I thought it might be safe, just this once. All I wanted was one quick glimpse of those plasmic bonfires 10,000 miles high leaping into space from the rim of the roaring sun. So I looked. And I saw them. It was a sublime and terrifying spectacle, which I can never forget. And my eyes survived, apparently unharmed, although a few years later I began to have trouble reading the numbers in a phone book, and my arms seemed too short to hold a newspaper far enough away from my eyes to make it readable.

"You need glasses," the eye doctor said. "You're farsighted."

"Why?"

"Middle age."

I told him about the time I stared at the sun face to face.

"You were lucky," he said.

August 22

Renée takes off for a three- or four-day tour of the park, leaving me here alone with my dirty dishes and the unswept floor. Two old-time park naturalists arrive, sit around drinking my coffee and telling what they call North Dakota jokes.

"Why won't a North Dakotan eat pickles?"

"Can't get his head in the jar."

"What does it say on the bottom of Coke bottles in North Dakota?"

"Open other end."

Etc. They do all the laughing.

Fog and rain, rain and fog. The fire season is shot to hell. Word from headquarters is that we're to be "terminated" (without prejudice) on September 5. Lookout completely socked in. Black bear with two cubs seen near Moose Wallow during my evening walk. Huckleberries, whortleberries, raspberries all ripening, but few of them.

The short-eared owl comes back at dusk, circling my glass-walled home. Perhaps it is me that silent bird is looking for. All my superstitions rise to the surface. At midnight under the full moon, dip your hand in the punky water of a hollow stump if you want to rid it of warts. Etc.

Cut and stack wood, refilling bin. Install new stovepipe. Caulk window frames. Repair broken shutters. Won't be here much longer.

One young punk showed up at nine-thirty this morning, jogging up the trail. Gasping for breath, before he even said hello he asked what time it was. So he could time his hike. A goggle-eyed bore with hairy legs, wearing track shorts and tennis shoes. Outward Bound type. He hung around for a few minutes, saw little interest in me or the lookout, and trotted down the trail again, vanishing into the clouds below.

Days now getting perceptibly shorter. Full moon rising over Rainbow Peak. Grand, gorgeous, shocking-pink sunset. Feel of autumn in the air. In August! Two golden eagles hovering on the sky, high above my cabin. God Bless America—Let's Save Some of It. Long live the weeds and the wilderness yet.

August 23

Rain, wind, rain, and fog. When the storm clears I see fresh snow on Kintla, Rainbow, and Reuter peaks, down to the 8,000-foot line. Temperature was 34° F this morning at 0630. Everything wet and slimy. Expect to see snails and other Mollusca crawling up the windowpanes. Horny octopi. . . .

August 24

Awoke this morning, after a long cold night, to find two inches of snow on the catwalk railing, on the pines, on everything in sight. Wet, fat snow, clinging to every twig and needle.

Renée returns, but only briefly. Has to leave at once for Vancouver. Her grandfather's dying. I am alone for the final week on this cold, dismal, rain- and snow-soaked mountain. I get so lonesome I wash the dishes for diversion. Loneliness. Mount Despair. Wintertime in August.

August 26

Termination date has now been advanced to August 28.

I go for long walks in the evening, hoping for one clear sight of GRIZ. The silence of the woods. No birds speak except one woodpecker, far below, hammering on a snag. But 1,000 feet below, under the snowline, the weather is late summer. Tufts of moss, like scalp locks, dangle from the branches of the lodgepole pine, the larch, the spruce. This is the forest primeval. Elaborate spiderwebs hang face-high across the trail, each with a tiny golden spider waiting at the center. Damp smells of fern and pine bark, the distant drumming of the woodpecker. Sounds like Red Norvo at the vibraphone. Bluebells still in bloom down here, wild roses covered with dew. Running water across the stones of the trail. I pause on the way back up to drink a handful; the sweet, cold, piney flavor reminds me of boyhood, the Allegheny Mountains back in old Pennsylvania. Lost at twilight in the green depths of the Big Woods.

Back to the cold darkness of the lookout cabin. I build a fire in the stove, sit with my feet on the open oven door and play the flute. The deer outside lift their heads to listen for a moment, then resume their feeding. Down in Arizona I used to rouse the coyotes at dawn, playing certain high notes on this silver-plated instrument. I'd play our tune and wait and after a few moments their wild cries came floating back to me across the desert, mimicking my song.

August 27

Last full day on the mountain. Sun shining for a change. Many deer hang about, fighting over my various urine-supplied salt deposits. Obvious pecking order among them: One old battle-scarred six-point buck is clearly dominant; the others keep their distance from him but jostle one another roughly.

Always looking and listening, these deer. Even the fawns have that wary look. Danger everywhere. Nor do they look well-fed, even now in late summer. Gaunt and ganted, lean and bony deer, how will they ever get through the coming winter? A tough life. Always hard times for deer. The struggle for existence. All their energy goes into survival—and reproduction. The only point of it all—to go on. On and on and on. What else is there? Sometimes I am appalled by the brutality, the horror of this planetary spawning and scheming and striving and dying. One no longer searches for any ulterior significance in all this; as in the finest music, the meaning is in the music itself, not in anything beyond it. All we have, it seems to me, is the beauty of art and nature and life, and the love which that beauty inspires.

Smell of cooking rubber. I withdraw my booted feet from the oven.

August 28

Raining again. Storm predicted. The packer with his mules is coming up the mountain this morning. I clean the lookout, put everything away, bolt the shutters back on the windows, pack our baggage, sign off on the radios. "This is Numa Ridge Fire Lookout going ten-seven [out of service] for about ten months. Have a good winter, everybody."

The packer arrives. Followed by the wind. We load the mules in a driving rain and start down the mountain.

Sacrificing Bathwater for the Cause

BRADLEY BLUM

IN THE EARLY DAYS of fire fighting, I'm told that lookouts were placed close enough together to allow them to hike to any fire within half a day and put it out themselves. These days, there are far fewer lookouts and it's generally left to others to fight the fires we locate. Once the fire is under attack, this places the lookout in the role of spectator—a role I sometimes find frustrating.

When I was hired by the Bureau of Land Management (BLM) in 1989, it was understood that my duty would be in the Bell Mountain Lookout. I was thirty years old, had never been a fire fighter, and though my weekly newspaper job wasn't lucrative, I wasn't giving it up to drive forty-five miles from Hailey to Shoshone to begin a new career in a job that paid $5.50 an hour. I saw the job as a summer respite from newspapering, a chance for solitude atop a 7,889-foot mountain.

Although I was not to be a fire fighter, when I began work for the BLM that summer I underwent the same training on fire behavior, safety, and procedures as the other rookies—mostly college kids. Because of my age and relatively good physical condition, I was given the training just in case. Later that first summer, requests for crews from the Shoshone District to go to fires on other BLM districts, as well as those on national forest land, depleted our forces to the point that there was concern about whether we could handle a fire in our own back-yard. As I went "in service" one morning at the lookout, I was told that my presence was required in Shoshone for standby fire-fighting duty. The roving lookout, a semiretired man who normally came to Bell

Mountain on my days off, would cover my post. The next few days served to dispel any thought I might have had about forgoing my perch atop Bell Mountain for the more exciting life of a fire fighter.

Most of the fire fighters on our district have, sooner or later, come up to Bell Mountain to deliver a truckload of water, have me sign some piece of paperwork, or just take a look around. (My lookout, like most of the BLM's, has a road leading to it.) Most comment on the magnificent view, which on a clear day can extend for 150 miles or more to include the Jarbridge Wilderness to the southwest in Nevada and the Bannock Hills beyond Pocatello to the southeast. Even on days when the haze above the Snake River Plain obscures these more distant ranges, there is a spectacular view to the north of Idaho's second-highest mountains, the Pioneers. Frequently, though, once these young men and women have taken in the view, they ask me if this isn't a boring job. I respond with a "no" smile, recalling that week on standby, and I think, but don't actually say, "You're the one with the boring job."

The act of suppressing a wildfire is quite exciting. (And I have, since that first season, had the good fortune to be sent to a forest fire in northwest Montana.) But, except for those occasional periods when the entire West seems to catch fire, most of the job is not fighting fires. If you work for the BLM, it's building or tearing out fences, repairing cattle guards or water pumps, painting, washing trucks, driving around on patrol, or otherwise doing or attempting to avoid busywork.

So until I or some other lookout can actually come up with a fire to fight, I consider my job far superior. When I'm not scanning the landscape for smoke or taking the daily weather readings, the time is mine to use as I see fit. Mostly, that means getting caught up on my reading, an unattainable goal. When the spirit moves me, I write. And I have a few little craft projects that never seem to be finished. I don't recall ever being bored with my job. But when the engines roll, I do occasionally wish I could take a more participatory role. I got my chance to do so near the end of that first season on Bell Mountain.

That year my "weekend" was Wednesday and Thursday. I returned to the lookout one Friday morning late in September to find a substantial cloud of thick, gray smoke rising from Dry Creek Canyon, which drains the south slope of Bell Mountain. I wasn't alarmed, because I'd been told about plans to do some controlled burning in a grazing allotment to improve cattle forage. Just the same, the amount of smoke was considerable, and I thought it at least merited a sarcastic remark. So when I went in service, I told the dispatcher, "Looks like I'd better get out my Pulaski."

No, I was assured, that wouldn't be necessary. Everything was under control. This was about noon.

The afternoon winds typically blow across the Silver Creek Valley from the southwest and slam into Bell Mountain's small range with enough force that a point to the west on the ridge serves as one of the best launch sites in the United States for hang gliders. By about one o'clock that day, the wind was blowing harder than usual, smoke was billowing out of the canyon, and the voices on the radio were beginning to sound a little strained.

By one thirty, the controlled burn was no longer controlled, and the range conservationist in charge of the project was wondering if the helicopter was available. It was, and the helicopter crew was dispatched. The next problem was finding water for the helicopter to drop on the fire. There isn't much in the way of surface water near my lookout under the best of circumstances, and 1989 was the third year of drought in southern Idaho and it was late summer. I heard someone on the radio ask how long it would take for a truck with water to get there from Shoshone. "At least an hour," came the response.

That's when I got my chance to step out of the role of spectator. As I mentioned, my water is trucked up to me. In those days I had a cylindrical container (originally used to ship jet airplane engines) that served as a water storage tank. The water was transferred from the truck into that tank, which held about seven hundred gallons, and I would use an electric paddle pump (my lookout has a propane-powered generator) to transfer water to a smaller tank on the deck of the lookout, thereby providing some pressure for my household system. It hadn't been too many days since I'd received my last shipment of water, and I believed the ground tank to be nearly full.

"Four-two-nine, this is Bell Mountain," I said, hailing the dispatcher on the radio.

"Bell Mountain, four-two-nine," came the response.

"I guess I could forgo my Saturday night bath if you guys want to take the water from here. I think the big tank's just about full."

There was a period of silence, and I could only imagine what was said in the dispatcher's office thirty-six miles away. When the silence was broken, it was conceded that the idea was worth trying, and the helitack crew was instructed to scout the mountaintop for a place to land.

A little while later, the helicopter came into view, hovered near the lookout, and then moved to the west just past the visitor parking area, landing on a sagebrush-covered knob. One of the helmeted figures, clad in the fire-resistant yellow shirt and green pants, was a friend of mine, Jeff Coupe. Normally he worked on the Forest Service's helitack crew base.

"Howdy, Jeff. When'd you become one of the good guys?" I yelled over the noise of helicopter and wind.

He smiled as he drew near and explained that he'd been detailed to the BLM's helitack crew for the remainder of the season.

We then set about figuring out how to get water out of the storage tank and into the "bambi bucket" that is slung under the helicopter to carry water to the targeted fire area. I showed Jeff the faucet on one end of the cylinder. We agreed that pumping water out of it would be too slow. The crew had unloaded a pump from the helicopter. Normally it is used to draft water from a surface source, such as a stream, pond, or lake, and pump it into the bambi bucket. However, the coupling on the end of the intake hose proved too large to fit inside the filler tube on top of my storage tank. I got some wrenches from my toolbox, and we attempted to remove the coupling. But the nuts were rusted to the bolts, and we eventually gave up, returning to my toolbox for a knife, and cut it off.

Without the hardware on the end, the hose fit snugly through the opening in the water tank. Once we overcame the engine's resistance to starting, we filled the bambi bucket, then watched the helicopter ferry it away with its contents dribbling from the bottom. It had become apparent that pulling water straight out of the tank into the bucket wasn't the best way to make the transfer, however. While the bucket was being filled, the helicopter had to hover just high enough to keep the bucket off the ground. Given the uneven terrain and gusting winds, the less time the helicopter had to hover, the better.

Then Jeff spotted my two thirty-gallon trash cans, and I quickly unloaded the plastic bag of trash from one and the recyclable contents from the other. We soon had in operation a system whereby we pumped the trash cans full of water while the helicopter was making a run for the head of the fire, which was visibly moving up the slope. When it returned, four of us would haul the full trash cans over to the bucket and dump in the contents.

Eventually more fire fighters showed up, and I was no longer needed to haul water. That's when my journalistic instinct took over. I got my camera and set about documenting this little drama. As it turned out, one of my color slides was used on the cover of the *Wood River Journal* the following week. I had been on the staff there for more than two years and had never gotten a color cover.

Andy Payne, the fire-control officer (the second-ranking fire-fighting position in a district), became the "incident commander" on the Bell Mountain Fire. For about an hour that afternoon, the lookout became the command center as Andy directed the attack against the blaze. The first priority was to stop the flames that were moving up the slope to the west before they hit the top of Bloody Ridge. On the other, north-facing, side of that ridge are stands of Douglas fir, some of them on private property.

The combined efforts of the crews on the ground doing shovel work and the helicopter making water drops eventually reduced the columns of flame to smoldering fingers that died out before reaching the ridge line. Once that was accomplished, Andy left the lookout, boarded the helicopter, and moved his command center to a ridge to the southwest where he had a view of the fire activity to the south. This part of the fire wasn't visible from the lookout because of an intervening ridge.

In the meantime, I listened to radio transmissions from an engine crew located on that ridge. The fire had run up to the road there and jumped it in a couple of places. The crew was trying to put out the flames on the uphill side of the road. If they failed, the fire only needed to cross the road one more time on its way to the lookout. Though the lookout is made of cinder block, steel, and glass and there isn't much vegetation at the very top of the mountain, the prospect of a wall of flame coming my way had me mentally reviewing the instructions about how to deploy the tinfoil bag known as a "fire shelter." As it turned out, though, the engine crew was able to douse the flames before the fire gained any momentum. So the fire shelter stayed in its little rectangular container.

As the day progressed, most of what I saw of the fire was smoke. The majority of activity took place near the base of the mountain in a couple of tributary gulches that form the upper end of the Dry Creek drainage. Because the lookout is situated in the middle of a relatively large, flat mountaintop, rather than on a precipice, I would not have been able to see most of the fire even without the intense smoke. I listened to the radio to find out what was going on below. Late in the afternoon, the air war was stepped up with the addition of a pair of retardant bombers. As a newspaper reporter covering public lands management, I'd been out on a few forest and range fires and seen most aspects of fire fighting, including the use of helicopters, but this was my first up-close view of bombers in action. I was impressed.

The retardant used in combating wildland fires is a red slurry mixture that sticks to vegetation and greatly reduces its flammability. In fire-fighting slang, the use of retardant is sometimes referred to as "painting" an area. The retardant is carried in World War II vintage bombers that look more suited for a stationary existence in a museum than flight. But fly they do. The retardant is held in compartments in the plane's fuselage and is released by opening those compartments individually. You frequently hear conversations on the radio between someone directing efforts on the ground and the bomber pilots regarding whether to paint an area ahead of a fire with another "door" or two.

Although that ridiculous movie *Always* has these pilots swooping down and clipping off the tops of burning trees to drop their loads, reality is still pretty incredible. Pinpoint accuracy is vital, since missing the mark doesn't do much to slow the advance of a fire and in some cases can be dangerous. Retardant slurry is considerably denser than water, and it travels at the speed of the airplane releasing it. There's a photograph hanging in Shoshone fire headquarters that shows a heavy (thousand-gallon capacity) fire engine that looks like it's been totally destroyed in a head-on collision—instead it was hit with a load of retardant and "painted" red. I don't recall how frequently it has happened, but in fire-fighter training we were told that people on the ground have been killed when hit by a retardant drop.

That afternoon on Bell Mountain, I watched these lumbering behemoths fly from the east down into the narrow canyons of Dry Creek, disappearing below the hills on either side just as the red cargo began to pour from their bellies. While I waited for what I thought was sure to be the sound of them crashing and exploding, they would miraculously reappear through a slim opening in the hills to the southwest and bank sharply to repeat the run and drop another door ahead of the blaze. I tried to watch this through my telescope, but couldn't see much because they were so close that it was difficult to track them quickly enough.

As the sun dropped toward the horizon, the bombers were "released" for the day and then returned to their base in Boise. Talk on the radio turned to how much longer the helicopters could stay in the air and what was being done about feeding the troops dinner. Though there was no talk about declaring the fire "contained" or "controlled," it was obvious that the day's efforts had turned the tide in our favor. Barring something like a sudden windstorm, the tense moments of getting a handle on the fire were behind the fire fighters and the drudgery of mopping up was ahead of them.

As it grew dark and fire fighters were being pulled off the lines, fed, and bedded down, I was still on duty. Normally I spent my Fridays reading the two local newspapers, which came out on Wednesday. With things settling down, I flipped on the light switch, waited for the generator to kick on, and then sat down with the newspapers.

I was feeling satisfied about the day's activities, about the fact that I was going to get several hours of overtime in before this thing was over, and that I'd been able to contribute more to this fire fight than I had to others. But I had one more important contribution.

I'd read a couple of pages into the *Journal* when I came across a story that was rather routine in nature. I'd written almost the same story at about the same time both the previous summers. As I read, it occurred to me that it might be a good idea to share the information with someone down below.

"Payne, Bell Mountain," I said into the open microphone.

"Bell Mountain, Payne," came Andy's response.

"Andy, did you guys bring the drinking-water supply up from Shoshone, or did it come from the fire station in Bellevue?"

"Hang on. I'll check."

Before Andy had a chance to ask around, someone else came on to say that the water had come from Bellevue.

"Why do you ask?" Andy inquired.

"I was just reading the paper here, and there's a story about how the bacteria counts are up and Bellevue and Picabo are on boil-water orders," I explained.

At that point, Andy passed the word that no one was to drink the water, and he sent a truck to Hailey to get another, safer, supply of water.

"Thanks, Brad," he said over the air. "I think you earned your pay today."

Death at High Noon

SUE CURTISS

I HAD BEEN watching him for several days. I have no idea where he spent his nights, but every morning, as I sat with my coffee in a sunny, sheltered corner of the catwalk, he would climb the post beside my head.

He was a handsome wolf spider. His head and legs were a deep, velvety black, and his body, about half the length of a 22 shell, was covered with short, thick, blue-gray fur.

He would climb the post cautiously, now and then standing on his hind legs to look at me with suspicion and a certain confidence. When he reached the rail he'd rest for a moment, his dark, streamlined body seeming to flatten itself against the wood. Then he'd move slowly along, avoiding the patches of early-morning dew, until he reached the splintered place where I'd thrown my hatchet at a packrat and missed.

Then he'd start spinning. Slowly, carefully, the fine silver thread trailing out behind him, he'd climb up and over the firmly attached splinter, his legs moving in intricate patterns too complicated for me to follow. When he'd finished he'd creep toward the bottom of the rail with the delicate silk, now well anchored by several wraps around the splinter, still trailing behind him.

I would watch until he disappeared under the rail, then, coffee gone, go back inside the lookout to take up the threads of my own day.

Once I stopped and looked under the rail to see what he was doing. His eyes glittered back at me from where he crouched motionless, almost invisible. He stared at me until I straightened and moved away.

One day, about three weeks after the start of our early-morning ritual, I took my lunch out to the catwalk. The sun was high and hot overhead; squirrels chattered below the tower, and bees hummed lazily in the mock orange under the steps.

A honeybee landed on my hand. I held very still, admiring the soft, glistening, greenish gold fur and the great black-faceted eyes. He walked across my hand, delicately tasting it now and then, and settled on my sandwich, the antennae and the long, impossibly thin tongue working busily to check out the exotic taste of mayonnaise and tuna fish. Losing interest, he buzzed over to the splintered place on the rail, then started down the post, tasting the wood and metal as he went. I laughed; he was so fat and bumbling and seemed so intent on exploring this new place he had found.

Then, in one startling instant, he became a blur of speed, sound, and color—a small golden ball spinning in a six-inch radius, his buzzing loud and continuous.

I watched, not really understanding what was happening.

The buzzing sounded and resounded; the only life, or movement, on that mountain was the small, golden body spinning in smaller and smaller circles.

The circles grew yet smaller, the spinning slowed and stopped, the tower was silent. A gauzy broken wing drifted down to rest beside my bare foot.

Reluctantly, I moved a little closer; stooped to look.

The bee hung from a slender silver thread three inches below the rail. Legs wrapped tightly around his prey, the spider stared back at me.

"Oh," I said. "So that's what you do."

I looked around for something, anything, to crush him with, and picked up my shoe. Then, after a moment, I dropped the shoe and went back inside. I poured another cup of coffee and brushed invisible fangs from the back of my neck.

Earthquake: Rustler Peak Lookout

Brenda Tippin

THE NIGHT WAS unusually black, scarcely illuminated by a sliver of moon slicing through the purple clouds. As my sixteen-month-old daughter lay sleeping, I listened. Not a sound. No wind. Not even a breeze.

Stillness caught somewhere in the back of my mind as I moved about the confines of my thirty-foot tower.

Again I listened. Only Trinity's breathing and that of Fuzzy Bear, our Rottweiler puppy, stirred in the heavy silence.

As I bent to adjust Trinity's covers, an eerie sensation registered. Some inner feeling I couldn't quite make sense of. There was not even a whisper of wind, yet the turning rods on the venetian blinds had begun to swing crazily back and forth.

The tower sort of groaned, and the floor lurched beneath my feet like the deck of a ship on a rolling sea.

Had the tower for some freak reason reached the limit of its endurance? Was it going to collapse with us inside? After all, the structure was forty-five years old.

Or perhaps something of extraordinary strength was down on the stairs trying to shake the tower. I rushed out on the catwalk to make sure the trapdoor was secure and peered anxiously into the gloom. There appeared to be nothing amiss, nothing at all, just the usual deer crunching the gravel under their feet in the parking lot below, looking for the crumbs I tossed down.

Only seconds passed, and the tower settled into a peculiar swaying

motion, both gentle and violent. Gentle because it felt like being
rocked in a giant cradle—an almost pleasant sensation were it not so
frightening. Violent because that is the only adequate word for the
extremely visible swaying motion of the tower, which stirs only slightly
in the strongest of winds.

The movement ceased as suddenly as it began, replaced once more
by that stillness. It was only then that I realized it must have been an
earthquake.

At about this time I received an anxious radio call from Butte Falls
Ranger Station confirming my supposition. Apparently the shock was
so strong there that they were worried about their houses falling down.
They were also concerned that nearby Mount McLoughlin, a dormant,
ninety-five-hundred-foot volcano, might erupt because of all the
disturbance.

I reported that we were okay despite the fact that we were in a
fourteen-by-fourteen-foot cab resting on thirty-foot wooden legs with
two-thirds of the wall space on all four sides devoted to windows. As
for McLoughlin, it too remained calm, a giant black silhouette against
night's blue curtain just to my south.

The fear in my spine gradually diminished and my legs and knees
regained their strength as I absorbed the fact that nothing dreadful had
happened. Both Trinity and Fuzzy Bear still slept.

Nothing at all was out of place, and in fact I might have thought
the whole thing the result of overworked imagination had I not just
talked to Butte Falls.

I then tuned in to KGO in San Francisco, since local stations were
too stunned to provide coherent information. I was shocked to hear
that the center of the quake had been pinpointed about fifteen miles
northwest of Klamath Falls, Oregon, barely thirty miles from me. There
were varying reports as to the strength of the jolt, but the U.S. Geologi-
cal Survey later reported it as 5.9.

Klamath Falls was in chaos. Windows had shattered in major stores,
many older buildings downtown had cracked and crumbled, a couple of
homes had actually collapsed, and there were two fatalities. The governor had declared Klamath County a disaster area.

Finally I went to bed, only to be roused by a second, stronger
shock (later measured at 6.0) at about ten of eleven. I looked toward
Klamath Falls, the lights of which send up a glow at night that can be
seen over the southeast ridge from Rustler.

I observed what appeared to be lightning bolts shooting up into the sky. I assumed this must be snapping power lines, and about this time a Klamath Falls woman called KGO's talkline. She reported that power transformers were blowing everywhere and the sky was lit up like the Fourth of July.

By this time I had recovered enough to feel a sense of God's peace and protection, and a realization came to me. Many buildings much more substantial than mine had suffered real damage because they lacked a simple thing I thought of as "give and take." Built on a rock foundation, my lookout is anchored by long cables on its four corners in such a way that it can bend and sway with the elements—even earthquakes—and when the shock has passed it still stands firm.

Gila Journal, New Mexico

DRUSILLA CLARIDGE

THE 1994 SEASON on the Gila National Forest was not an easy one. Day after day came dry lightning and temperatures ten degrees above normal. But worst were the deaths: two fire fighters and their pilot in a helicopter crash, then fourteen fire fighters in Colorado.

As a former member of the Forest Service family, I could read between the lines of the news reports. Everything came back to me: the long, hot days; the waiting for a voice over the radio to say that the fire fighters were on the fire, or safely home.

I was a lookout on the Gila for three seasons. For two of those years I kept a journal. Perhaps entries from it will explain why, five years after leaving that line of work, I still think about going back, even after this deadly and arduous fire season.

The spring after I graduated from college, I was offered a lookout job on the Glenwood Ranger District. My post was Bearwallow, a tower situated at an altitude of 9,953 feet in the Mogollon Mountains and accessible by a good road. I wanted the job so much that I confided to no one that I was terrified of talking on the radio.

From Bearwallow, you can see mountain ranges in all directions: westward is Mount Graham; to the south, the Mogollons; the Saliz and Tularosa mountains to the north; and Black Mountain to the east. Beyond Black Mountain is the Black Range, marking the eastern edge of the forest.

The Gila National Forest is 3.3 million acres in size and includes the Gila Wilderness ("First of them all," we brag here) and the Aldo Leopold Wilderness in the Black Range. It is contiguous with the Apache Sitgreaves National Forest, and the two, combined with the Coconino, the Tonto, and the Kaibab, make up the largest ponderosa pine forest in the world. The casual visitor may not comprehend the dryness, the rugged nature of the country, and the distances. At least once a year a lost hiker perishes.

Most fires on the Gila are lightning-started. In the spring, while the snow in the high country is melting and running off, the wind blows hard. It uproots last year's tumbleweeds, eliminates nearly all the moisture from the earth, and often fills the air with dust. In June, when the hot air from the surrounding deserts rises and mixes with the cool air in the mountains, thunderheads build over the peaks. These thunderheads may produce electrical storms—lightning accompanied by little or no rain.

This is when the fire fighters work overtime. Extensive piñon, juniper, pine, and fir forests, in country that is mostly straight up and down, combined with extreme heat and dryness, produce fire-fighting conditions as dangerous as those Norman Maclean described so well in *Young Men and Fire.*

For a lookout, the work may go to sunset, and beyond. The radio is hyperactive during these "fire busts."

The job is more complex than it may sound. In some parts of the forest, giving a smoke a meaningful legal description is an act of conjuring in itself. This is particularly true of the Black Range, a chain of mountains a hundred miles long. It is so rugged that it has never been completely mapped.

The summer I was on Bearwallow was one of little fire activity. I knew the job could be demanding, that I might have to turn in many smokes, keeping a log of both fires and radio traffic. I didn't trust myself to locate smokes as well as I knew was needed, so was relieved that lookouts more experienced than I were stationed on Saddle Mountain, Negrito Peak, Eagle Peak, and Mogollon Baldy. I let them take the lead.

One afternoon Negrito Peak turned in a smoke right under my nose. (It's a curious thing that lookouts often can't see a fire on their own mountain.) Negrito Peak was seeing smoke coming out of Mineral Creek, on the south side of Bearwallow. I watched, astonished, as dispatch sent a helicopter crew, a ground crew, and smoke jumpers. I couldn't even see the smoke.

Later I learned that Mineral Creek was one of "those places"—so steep and altogether nasty for fire fighters that dispatch sent in a maximum of attack forces. Actually, I had seen the forerunner of that fire during my lunch hour. A puff of hot gas had come up out of Mineral Creek, momentarily distorting the view across the gorge. But that was all, and I didn't realize what I'd seen until Negrito Peak turned it in.

By studying the smokes and the legals given for them, by observing the country with my naked eyes and through binoculars, by comparing everything I saw against maps, I began to see how the job was done.

In this my first lookout job, I learned a lot from the lookouts on Negrito Peak, a husband and wife who were old hands. A highlight of that season was sitting under the Negrito tower with them, drinking beer and taking turns hand-cranking ice cream.

During my last week at Bearwallow, I was on the radio constantly, serving as the communications link between dispatch and a fire burning on Iron Creek Mesa. It was a controlled burn that had blown out and was approaching private property. Fire camp was in Willow Creek. They had no contact with anyone but Bearwallow. During that week I learned the secret to radio communications: *Repeat everything back.*

I left Bearwallow feeling good. I had listened and watched and learned. I had overcome radio shyness. In my innocence, I often looked east and wished I were working on Black Mountain.

I dredge these things up from memory, as I kept no journal on Bearwallow. I can't recall having a problem with the solitude there. But I must have, because the following winter I got married and gave up lookout work.

This is not the place to explore the anatomy of a dysfunctional marriage. I will say that mine was the genuine article. It felt a lot like spending too much money on a pair of boots that don't fit. For eight years I was paralyzed by dual needs. I wanted to belong, just like I'd wanted to fit into the mainstream in college. But I also needed solitude, and to be able to decide for myself what was right for me.

What *was* right for me? I hadn't a clue. Clearly, something had to be done. I began a twelve-step recovery program; I began to keep a daily journal.

By the spring of 1988, it looked certain that those expensive boots were never going to fit. Still, the relationship was a hard habit to break, and I didn't know if I was ready for a divorce. A good way to test it would be to return to lookout work. The tower available to me? Black Mountain.

My work schedule was ten days on and four days off. The amenities were what they had been at Bearwallow: a tiny cabin with propane lights, refrigerator, and hot plate; a cistern and hand pump; an out-house; and a glass room atop three flights of stairs. Once again I took sponge baths and washed my hair in a metal basin.

The lone bulk of Black Mountain rises just off the southern end of the Plains of San Augustin, between the headwaters of the East and Middle Forks of the Gila River. Working there presented greater challenges than Bearwallow. Foremost among these was getting there. The drive to Beaverhead Work Station was an hour on paved road, then two on dirt roads. I stopped at Beaverhead to leave my groceries; they were packed up to me later. I drove another twenty minutes to the trailhead, and from there I walked two hours to the tower at 9,287 feet. Altogether it was a six-hour commute.

Visitors had been frequent at Bearwallow, located as it was in a heavy-use area on a good road. Black Mountain was neither of these. Although certain trails funnel large numbers of hikers into the Wilderness, the Black Mountain trail isn't one of them. The occasional visitor was usually a hunter, scouting for the fall elk hunt.

Beaverhead Work Station, the nearest outpost, is so remote, so far from anywhere, that power lines were not brought in until 1990. When I worked at Black Mountain, in 1988 and 1989, the Forest Service and ranches still derived their electricity from diesel generators.

I had some things to learn about the country, including the ill-mapped Black Range mountains, but this time I was willing to make mistakes and learn from them.

Some smokes made me look stupid and there was nothing to be done about it. The smoke that came up out of Murtocks Hole, for example. From my viewpoint it was on the other side of Brushy Mountain, and I had no way of knowing how far behind Brushy it was or which side of the Gila River it was on. No amount of studying the country was going to help me. The best thing I could do was assign the smoke a section somewhere on my azimuth as it crossed over the smoke.

Of course, I gave it the wrong section. When the spotter on board the helicopter saw where it actually was and the dispatcher gave me the correct section number, all I could do was sigh and say, "I copy."

Another time, I attempted to turn in a smoke off the southeast side of Mogollon Baldy. This mountain is 10,770 feet. The lookout tower there is the highest on the Gila, and the women up there really know what they're doing. In turning in this smoke, I was informed by one of the women that I couldn't possibly see into where I said the smoke was. I gave her my azimuth and let her figure it out.

By the time I began work at Black Mountain, I had been keeping my journal every day for a year. More than ever, I felt torn by dual needs. I thirsted for the mountains, and for a closeness I didn't have in my marriage. At Black Mountain I wrote this out. I wrote and wrote. Every thought went into the journal. When I reread these journals, it all comes back to me: the weather, the wildlife, the fires, the sense of wonder that made the loneliness worthwhile.

May 27. I decided writing has the quality of prayer.

June 9. I heard the chipmunks out on the porch last night. It sounded like a good time. Pretzels and beer. Stomping around.

June 11. After the rain the waterdogs coming up from Willow and Iron Creeks glowed like opals in the setting sun. That country is sky-lined. After sunset, the light on the storm clouds turned the whole world a gentle, glowing orange. The same color as the waterdogs, come to think of it.

June 16. Elk nearby this morning. I scouted with the camera: smelled them and saw fresh dung, but didn't see them. I did see a bull elk night before last, down on the Wolf Hollow trail.

July 12. A thunderstorm moved up on Black Mountain last night, and I saw a triple rainbow, with another separate rainbow above that. I wanted to get a photo, but by the time I changed film, the lightning was hitting too close. The thunder makes noise I can hear clear through my body. One stroke of lightning zapped either the tower or the cabin; I heard a sizzling and then saw the flash at the same time as the thunder crashed. I ducked my head reflexively, as if to crawl under the table and get away from it. The storm dumped a little over half an inch of rain.

July 14. I just heard a bear. A tumbling of rocks.

July 24. Last night when I saw the summer moonlit sky, I regretted all the time I have ever spent indoors.

By the end of the summer, both my husband and I were relieved to be apart, and I asked for a divorce. For me, the hardest part was wondering how in the world I was going to make it alone. I found a part-time job and stuck ever closer to my journal.

The next year, 1989, I was back on Black Mountain tower. The forest had not been so dry in thirty-five years. Two of the largest fires were the Divide at ten thousand acres and the Shelley at twelve thousand acres, both ignited by lightning and put out only by the summer rains.

The Divide Fire was a bad one, with extreme fire behavior, its own weather, and even a wildlife management crisis. Ash from the fire polluted Diamond Creek, a key habitat of the endangered Gila trout. The surviving fish, one-fifth of the total population, had to be relocated immediately.

Because of the extreme dryness, I was plagued by rodents. They stole the dog food and chewed on the cabin walls at night. I had to set out traps and poison, not something I like to recall.

And sometimes that long commute on dirt roads defeated me. One spring evening I left Beaverhead for home. Taking an unfamiliar route, I came around a corner in Railroad Canyon and bogged down in the sand.

I didn't know how often the road was used. I did know it was the largest blank space on the New Mexico map. I might not be found for days. I had little water, no food, no flashlight.

I got out of my car to look for the lights of a ranch house. There was no moon. It was dark, dark. After forty-five minutes of stumbling up a hill, the top of which revealed only more dim hills and a starry sky, not an electric light to be seen, I retreated to my car.

At one in the morning, I started it up to run the heater. At two in the morning, headlights appeared on the road ahead. I leaped out to flag the vehicle down. A Cochiti Pueblo man and his two nephews, coming in for a spring turkey hunt, peered suspiciously at me from the cab of their pickup. The man refused to try to pull my car out but agreed to take me to Beaverhead.

When the crew boss brought me back in the morning, the Forest Service truck easily pulled my car out of the sand. I jumped in and drove away, leaving my purse on the seat of the truck. When I discovered its absence, halfway across the Plains of San Augustin, I didn't care. I was alive. Things like that helped me keep my priorities straight.

The journaling helped, too. I was into it full blast by then. It gave a place to work out all my thoughts about myself, about relationships, about the job I was doing. No one told me what to think, feel, or do in my journal. So I wrote it all down.

April 22. When the wind blows, needles fall on the tin roof of the cabin. I'd forgotten about that little detail.

April 24. Today was glorious. The great ranges, the deep canyons, the rock, the sky, the blue distances. I've said I won't come back next year. Now I don't know. Let me stay for*ever.*

April 26. Life is powerful slow up here. I can take a whole afternoon to write one letter.

May 1. At the helispot today I saw a big red-tailed hawk land on a pine tree not 50 feet from me. I stood on the path below and waited. I could see the swallows diving in the air above the tower. Then the hawk took off with the quietest swish of wings and flew around the west shoulder of the mountain. I shaded my eyes from the setting sun with my hand and saw the hawk catch an updraft from the head of Jordan Canyon. She lifted above the tree tops and hung in the air, side-slipping, then she began to drop. The last I saw of her, her talons were extended below her and her wings were folded into her body.

May 3. There is a place in my mind that belongs to where the forks of the Gila come together. There, where the river bends around Granite and Copperas Peaks, with Tadpole Ridge looming in the distance and green North Mesa standing before, this place I know.

May 16. Morning. Snow on the ground. It's pretty. The dog keeps looking at me as if it's my fault. I kept hearing stuff falling on the cabin roof last night—I thought it was rain. Today I'm happy to be here. Too bad I don't have company.
Evening. Well, I was wrong. I've said I don't get bored, but I do. When I'm bored, I begin arguing with people who aren't here.

June 10. Big fire going. I've never seen one puff up black, right away, like this one did. This one was man-caused, by a spark from heavy equipment.

June 21. Few clouds, lots of smoke.

June 22. The Shelley Fire, 28 miles away, is really smoking. I can see and smell it up here this morning.

June 23. Evening. The swallows did some wild flying today. They were feeding at the head of Trap Corral Canyon when I came back from my walk. I could see them below me, dancing specks in the evening sun. Trying to describe this mountain is like trying to describe the wind in the aspen or what it was like that morning I woke in the dusk before dawn, when I slept in the tower to get away from the rodents. A gust of wind, a shower of rain on the glass, a lens of red in the east.

June 25. The Shelley Fire is 11,000 acres.

June 28. Swallows whistle by the tower, ravens wheel and tumble by on the wind. But there is too much aloneness, hardly any limit to it.

July 2. The Divide Fire is burning over the ridge northwest of Diamond Peak, on the crest of the Black Range. The fire is 25 miles away. I can see a line of retardant along the top of that ridge. Kelly was up early this morning with my groceries, and she shook her head. She said she didn't know how they would catch it—it's in heavy fuels.

July 3. Too hot to sleep with the door closed last night, but the wind kept blowing it shut. Wakeful, I heard a report from the Divide Fire. It wasn't windy over there, which I thought was odd. They were reporting extreme fire behavior and this in the middle of the night when fires usually calm down.

4:30 p.m. No wonder my nose is bleeding. The relative humidity is seven percent.

July 4. We're having a lot of lightning after dark. "Dark as a dungeon and lightning all around," my boss just reported on the radio. He spotted a grass fire in the hills on the east side of the Black Range and described it as a "wall of fire."

July 6. Have been listening all day to the shuffling of crews and gear and food and lost jumpers.

It sure is easier to shoot at the chipmunks after they've kept me awake all night. I think I just got one. It's hot. There's no air stirring. The dog pants, gets up and takes a drink, lies back down and pants.

July 9. Evening. Lightning hitting close, purple and yellow. Standing on the step of the cabin, protected by the overhanging roof, I am lit by the gas lamp behind me in the cabin, and the zag of lightning beyond the trees.

July 13. They took 566 Gila trout out of Diamond Creek today. They're taking them to the Mescalero hatchery.

July 24. I think the "monsoons" have arrived. It's raining.

July 26. It poured from 8:30 to 9:30 last night. Hillsboro Peak tower will be closing in the next few days.

August 2. A hot day. It showered around noon, but the day was mostly clear. Some rain in the distance, north and east.

August 3. Had dinner with the trail crew last night. We poured blueberry pie filling into a foil-lined dutch oven, covered the fruit with batter, and put the lid on. After the steaks came off the fire, we screwed the dutch oven down into the coals and then Kelly shoveled coals on top. Twenty-five minutes later, blueberry cobbler.

August 7. I came upstairs last night because the night was so pretty and I wanted to watch the distant thunderstorms. They were way off, flashing constantly. One was over the Rio Grande Valley, and one was in Arizona, perhaps over the Gila Valley.

August 8. A heavy shower, over a half inch of rain. It started here and moved west across Yellow Mountain to the Middle Fork and Lilley Mountain. There's another cloud to the east.

August 9. One more day and the job is over.

I left Black Mountain and didn't return. I moved to Santa Fe and went to massage school. There I began to make friends with the troublesome loner side of myself. After practicing massage in a group classroom environment, one belongs whether one wants to or not.

This part of me, the part that wants to live alone on a mountain peak, is the same part that caused my chest to ache one day, an ache that was alleviated only by starting work on a novel. This self enabled me to sit at a computer four to six hours a day for almost two years and write that first novel. And I continue to keep my journal.

Recently I spoke to the crew boss at Beaverhead. He mentioned that Black Mountain will be open next year.

I remember what it was like to see thousands of acres of forest burning, to see the lightning strike that started it, the human courage that contained it, and the act of nature that put it out.

I remember the sound of the aspen leaves in the wind, the comfort I took in the millions of acres of empty land. There was plenty of time to watch the unfolding days and nights, and to ride them, as though I lived on a gentle wind.

I remember being alone for days on end. At times the silence beat at my eardrums. I was lonely, and the loneliness wouldn't go away. I used to wonder whether I was running away from life or toward it.

I know myself better now. I know that it doesn't take much socializing to satisfy me. I also know that I want to write and draw and paint. Imagining another season on a lookout tower, from the perspective of a burgeoning creative life, makes me again want to ride on that gentle wind.

I believe I will go back to Black Mountain.

In Memorium: Sean Gutierrez, Sam Smith, Robert Boomer

A Day on Coolwater Lookout: Some Thoughts on Vertigo, Cougars, and Talking to Coyotes

Jackie Johnson Maughan

0530. Enormous bull moose feeding in Fire Lake, which is about six hundred feet down the mountain from me. At first he looked like a half-submerged log. Then the log moved and raised its head and water streamed from its huge rack and bottom plants hung from its mouth. When the moose leaves about an hour later—I don't notice exactly when—there's this wake of stirred-up mud marking exactly where he's been.

0700. Early morning is the best time . . . before the radios get busy and the visitors (I call them tourists if in a bad mood) show up. The fire lookout is located on the big east-west ridge between the Lochsa and Selway rivers. It's a fifty-four-hundred-foot climb up fourteen miles of bad road, especially the last two miles, but still people come. "Don't you get lonely up here?"

One man came up with his rifle rack and moose permit and wanted to know if I'd seen any wildlife. "Nope," I said, scratching my head and looking sorrowful. "Haven't seen a thing except a couple of whitetails down by where the road gets bad."

0800. "Fenn Ranger Station, this is Coolwater—morning check-in." I have both the Nez Perce and Clearwater radios since the boundary between the two forests is on this ridge. In fact, on the map it looks like it goes right down the middle of my lookout.

0910. Nez Perce Fire Dispatch—weather: sunny and hot, temps 84-97, LAL 2-3, Haines 4 . . . LAL means Lightning Activity Level, with the highest danger being 6. The Haines Index refers to the condition of the fuel load on the ground; a 4 is pretty dry, and if lightning strikes, the conditions are ripe for fires.

You determine where smokes are by using the fire finder—a portion of the forest map mounted on a large disk on a cabinet in the middle of the lookout. On this map, Coolwater is the center of the universe. The fire finder really dominates my small space here and looks like an altar or something.

The first week on the lookout is really very strange, and apparently the person before me left after eight days. I'm not sure how to describe it, but the vastness of the land is intimidating. So is the wind, which blows almost constantly.

Maybe it's a kind of vertigo of space. There are windows on all four sides down to about my knee level. The space asserts itself in a way that's like climbing a mountain, only it's with you twenty-four hours a day. It's like living in a box of wind and light. Think about it this way: Normally when you see hawks and eagles, you're looking up at them. That's why the bird books show such detailed pictures of their undersides. Up here, though, you're often looking down at them or maybe at eye level—a nice thought ("and she stared eye to eye with the noble eagle"), but it is, in fact, disorienting—a contrast of the small (at times prisonlike) space of the lookout itself, versus the space of the nine or ten million acres of wilderness and forest land visible on all sides of you.

0922. Coyote calling from 19 Mile Ridge. I answer and it shuts up. Did I say something wrong? I figure out much later that I probably sounded too aggressive. I did get it to talk to me eventually, after I learned to mimic its cry in volume, duration, and pitch. If you want to talk to a coyote, don't sound bigger than it is, like you're something that might want to eat it. This guy got so he would talk to me for up to half an hour. No, I don't know what he was saying, but I was saying that he ought to come up and see me. He never did.

2015. "Fenn, Indian Hill, Coolwater, this is Harrison," comes a scared voice. She's trying to raise anybody she can.

"Harrison, Coolwater," I answer.

She's camped out alone in her sleeping bag, no tent. She's been marking timber in a steep brushy drainage in Saddle Creek. She was wakened by the feel of something sniffing at her—a cougar.

The cat backs off, circles, approaches, snarls, backs off again.

"Harrison, Coolwater—do you have your boots on? No? Put your boots on and stand up. Maybe if it sees how big you are it will go away." (I wonder to myself, how big is she?) "Did you try the squelch on your radio?" Yes, she tried that. Also banging pots together.

"Harrison, Coolwater—what's it doing now?"

"It's lying down looking at me."

"Have you got your boots on?"

"I'm putting them on now. Oh, he's gotten up again. He's circling toward me."

"Harrison, I'm going to radio Fenn for advice." Hell, I don't know what to tell her; I haven't been in this kind of cougar country before. Fenn can't hear her cause she's in a pocket. I'll have to relay.

"He's really a beautiful animal," she says.

I relay back to her with instructions to build a fire. Then, after consultation, she's instructed instead to slowly and politely exit.

She doesn't seem too wild about this idea, since it's close to last light and there's not much of a moon, and the country is steep and brushy.

2047. Harrison's boss comes on; I'm to tell her to stay where she is. Exit would be through heavy brush in the dark. At least where she is she has some visibility. They're sending some people in to get her. She's to build a fire and get a big stick, and look forward to a sleepless night.

2049. I volunteer to stay up with her and talk. She thinks that's a good idea. I tell her I'll read her some poetry.

2101. They're sending a couple people in to get her—instruct her to get enough wood so she doesn't have to move around after dark. Also, since she doesn't have any spare batteries, not to transmit too much.

Yes, but can I read to her on channel 2 since receiving doesn't take as much juice as transmitting?

Better not, better keep the channel clear. Do check in with her every fifteen minutes, however. (This to make sure she hasn't been eaten, her boss says.)

2119. Two people will be there in about three hours. Coming in by O'Hara Ridge.

2129. About one and a half hours till people (John and Ken) can contact her by radio.

2143. Harrison, Coolwater—she's drowsing by the fire; has almost fallen asleep. Cat has circled into the brush and she hasn't seen it for a while.

2300. John and Ken have made radio contact with her. She's kind of embarrassed that all this hoopla's going on.

(Find out later that John and Ken were told to shoot the cat. They didn't find it. Harrison's all right; I hear her on the radio the next day and she's right back out there alone marking timber.)

2315. Well, there's a trapdoor in the catwalk of my lookout. It's really heavy and I always close it and latch it at night, but tonight I actually chain it closed, which is absurd, I know, but there you have it.

A Season of Fire

DON SCHEESE

Saturday, August 20. For a lookout, Saturday night is like any other evening. I sign off on the two-way radio at 6 P.M., eat dinner, take a walk, return to the tower and read until darkness, then fall asleep. But sometime later an unmistakable scent of woodsmoke jolts me awake. I look north, the direction of the wind, and in spite of a waxing moon I can make out an orange glow behind the silhouette of Grassy Ridge in Hells Canyon. Fire! I note the time—10:15 P.M.—and take a bearing of the fire to determine its location. Then I radio Dispatch Headquarters in McCall, and give my report: "There is a fire burning in Hells Canyon in the vicinity of Sawpit Creek, about five miles north of the lookout. My azimuth is 342 degrees. The legal location is Township 21 North, Range 3 West, Section 4. I can't see the base of the fire but my guess is that it's about fifty acres right now."

It's the worst possible scenario. Because it's dark, firefighters can't be flown to the fire; it will take three to four hours for trucks to drive to the scene; and steep and rugged terrain with explosive cheatgrass fuels the Snake River floor. Combine the current high winds and you have a tinderbox condition.

Sunday, August 21. Events take on a surreal, blurry quality. All night and into the morning I relay calls from fire crews in the depths of the canyon to McCall Dispatch, and provide updates on the fire. In the darkness there is little for the crews to do except evacuate fishermen, campers, and river-runners. Fanned by northwest gusts, the fire races up grassy slopes into Douglas-fir and ponderosa pine, and occasionally burning debris tumbles downhill onto the Idaho Power road that dead ends at Hells Canyon Dam where rafters put in.

By morning the fire rages across seven hundred and fifty acres. Most fires a lookout reports remain small—one tenth of an acre in size—and usually require three to four helitackers or smokejumpers to handle them. But this fire, the "Eagle Bar Fire" (so named because it apparently started near Eagle Bar on the Snake River) has become a Class I fire, meaning top fire management personnel from across the country will be assigned to contain and suppress the blaze. Four hundred firefighters in twenty-person crews have been called for, and a fire camp is to be established at Kinney Point, three miles north of the lookout. War has been declared.

Retardant planes lumber overhead, making drop upon drop to halt the advancing fire. Pilots' calls to Dispatch—"heading to McCall for reload and return"—become a familiar refrain. But things begin to go awry in the afternoon. The air attack plane reports that the lead plane (used to guide in the ponderous retardant planes) has just crashed in the backwaters of Hells Canyon Dam. Air operations are then shut down until another lead plane can be found. In the meantime the fire grows, whipped by winds and heated by soaring afternoon temperatures.

By early evening Horse Mountain becomes a helibase for the numerous helicopters shuttling crews to various locations on the fire. Word finally gets out that the pilot of the downed lead plane walked away, or rather swam, from the crash to a nearby island.

Tuesday, August 23. An August dog-day dawns, sultry and still. Smoke hangs in the air. At 7:30 A.M. I hear the thwock-thwock-thwock of the first helicopter feeling its way through the pall. The smoke is too thick for retardant planes to make their drops safely in the canyon narrows, so we wait for the wind to lift the inversion.

I meet firefighters from all over the country. We all complain about the hornets, which are thick as the smoke, and chased from their nests by the fire, even more bad-tempered than usual. Everyone gets stung, and some, unknowingly allergic, are medivacked by helicopter to the hospital in McCall.

Wednesday, August 24. Choppers again appear through the smoky haze of sunrise. I find out the cause of the fire: a motorcyclist in the canyon who tried to burn his toilet paper. Everyone has a good laugh. Black humor dominates on fires as a way of keeping everyone loose in otherwise dangerous and dirty conditions.

Later in the day another lead plane is dispatched to the Eagle Bar

Fire but then diverted to a new start on the Salmon National Forest. The rationale of the Forest Service is that it's better to divert personnel and equipment to a small fire so it might be contained quickly and prevented from becoming yet one more large fire, than to throw all one's resources at a large fire that may burn uncontrolled despite all efforts. Makes a certain amount of gloomy, perverse sense.

A firefighter on the line collapses from heat exhaustion. The column of smoke towers to 12,000 feet creating its own cumulus. With binoculars I can see trees torching off like matchsticks on the slopes of Sheep Rock and Kinney Point. Then at 5:20 P.M. it becomes official: fire camp is evacuated from Kinney Point to Horse Mountain. A strategic retreat. The rest of the day, helicopters shuttle crews from the fire to the ridgetop where I live. The invasion begins.

On the road to the lookout, National Guard trucks ferry equipment and crews; tractor-trailers haul food and shower units. Steam-cleaned Idaho Fish and Game tank-trucks transport potable water while water trucks sprinkle down the dust, and caravans of green Forest Service pickups and vans appear. At dusk an F-4 jet screams over the fire on a mission of infra-red reconnaissance. So much for my summer of wilderness solitude.

Thursday, August 25. Latest estimate of the fire—2,100 acres. I hear this report during my tour of "Horse City," as the fire camp is now dubbed. Declaring myself benevolent mayor-dictator of the new metropolis (population 700), I stroll along "Main St.," past rows of porta-potties, a food trailer and kitchen, mess tents, and shelters representing the various facets of a large fire organization: Plans, Communications, Finance, Logistics, Supply, Ground Support, First Aid. On the fringes, slightly removed from the drone of generators and the glare of lights, are the camps of the twenty crews assigned to the fire. On the southeast point of the mountain are the helibase, the landing spots for the helicopters working the fire, and the camps of the helitack crews. Overnight, Horse City has become a sizable Idaho town with a restaurant, bank, and airport.

Friday, August 26. Firestorm. One of the Overhead Team tells me just after midnight the fire suddenly shifted direction, trapping twenty to thirty firefighters. As a result they have to deploy their fire shelters, one-person A-frame tents made of an aluminum foil-like insulation. Absolutely the ultimate nightmare for a firefighter. Yet, incredible as it seems, the crew members are exchanging jokes over the radio. Only one injury reported: a dollar-size burn on the calf. By 3:30 A.M. the fire comes within two and a half air miles of the lookout. Then the smoke obscures the view so there is nothing to do but go to bed, though sleep is fitful.

Following breakfast I find out the crews who had to deploy their fire shelters are being shipped to McCall today for trauma therapy, apparently standard procedure for anyone who has gone through such an ordeal. The decision comes down that no crews are to be sent on the line—conditions are too smoky, too uncertain, and hence too dangerous. So firefighters do laundry, play hacky-sack, read newspapers, magazines, and junk literature from the library, and stock up on candy bars and pop. I take my first shower in two months—feel almost human again. The camp crew fashions a large sign that reads "MAYOR OF HORSE CITY" and hangs it at the base of the tower. I spend much of the day mingling with my constituents.

At a fire camp one of the ways to pass the time is to check out people's t-shirts. On a large fire it's customary for commemorative t-shirts to be designed and sold. My favorite is from one of the Yellowstone fires. With a firestorm for a backdrop, Boo-Boo says to Yogi the Bear, "Yogi, Mr. Ranger isn't gonna like this."

Saturday, August 27. Fire estimated at 3,100 acres. It begins to make runs to the east, up toward White Monument Ridge, torching the archaeological remains of the old mining town of Helena and the site of the Peacock Mine near the head of Copper Creek. The big concern now is that the fire will make a run into Deep Creek, a sinuous steep, heavily-timbered tributary of the Snake River where there are no roads and it's too dangerous to place firefighters. Once the fire becomes established there, forget it; there will be no choice but to let it burn into the Hells Canyon–Seven Devils Wilderness.

Sunday, August 28. Another windy day, and the fire blows up again, this time in Copper Creek. Retardant planes are ineffective because it's too smoky for them to fly low enough, and the wind scatters their "mud" before it reaches hot spots. Three helicopters with their water-buckets are somewhat more effective.

Early in the evening I fly over the fire in a helicopter with the district ranger. First we inspect Grassy Ridge, where backburning has begun. The entire ridge is now charcoaled. Next we fly through Hells

Canyon. Though at first glance it appears there is nothing to burn, it's evident that along the canyon walls something is burning. On closer inspection we can see what it is—lichen-draped rocks. In Deep and Copper Creeks there is no question what is burning—timber, and lots of it. There the fire has created a green and black mosaic of Douglas-subalpine fir, ponderosa pine, and Englemann spruce. We climb up Deep Creek through billowy smoke clouds and over conifers crowning out in flames. On the return we get a spectacular view of Horse Mountain—a tent-city on a hill.

Monday, August 29. The media discovers the Eagle Bar Fire. Cameramen and reporters from a Boise TV station appear in camp and seek out interviews (including one with the lookout who reported the fire), and an information officer from the Payette National Forest arrives to take photographs and talk with people.

Tuesday, August 30. The fire slops over White Monument Ridge into Camp Creek, adding an entirely new dimension to the containment strategy. Camp Creek is a tributary of Indian Creek; and Indian Creek runs through the tiny mining town of Cuprum, only two miles south of the lookout. And on another front it's now official: the fire has entered the wilderness area. Which means that the Wallowa Whitman National Forest of Oregon is involved, since it administers that portion of the forest.

Following breakfast I make the rounds, scanning the bulletin board (which lists reports of fires across the country) and visiting the tents of Plans and Communications, hoping to glean some new information about the fire. More than thirty injuries have now occurred, mostly bee stings. Latest estimate of size: 7,400 plus acres. The "plus" has me concerned. The Eagle Bar Fire has now become the number one priority fire in Region 4 of the Forest Service. Ten more crews have been requested, but with the Yellowstone infernos it's unlikely we'll get them.

Wednesday, August 31. After I turn in my morning weather observations to Dispatch they tell me I was on one of the Boise news programs last night, announced as "The Mayor of Horse City."

The fire has acquired a ho-hum quality in spite of the fact it has yet to be contained and there is no projected date of containment. As in war, destruction becomes routine, almost mundane. People are actually talking about demobilization. This fire is no longer exciting and new; it's old and boring. Chatting with various crew members, the unanimous sentiment is that everyone wants to go on to a new fire—where things won't be any easier or less dangerous. Just different.

Thursday, September 1. Rumor mongers hard at work. Camp to bug out in a few days. Camp to remain for weeks. Hard to get a straight answer these days. Much depends on whether most of the fire can be confined to the wilderness. If so, it will be allowed to burn within certain parameters and merely a skeleton crew will be on hand to monitor its progress. Allowing a human-caused fire to burn unchecked into a wilderness area? The hard truth is, there's not much we can do about it.

Following the morning weather forecast, dispatch gives the fire situation report. Acreage of the fires burning in Yellowstone: North Fork, 109,000 acres; Wolf Lake, 40,000; Fan, 23,000; Clover Mist, 213,000; and Snake River, 186,000. In comparison, the Eagle Bar Fire of 8,000 acres is but a flicker.

Another dog day. Smoke lies like a lid on top of valleys and mountains. Visibility down to two miles. If there were other fires out there they'd remain burning, undetected, until they became too big and out of control. Fortunately we've had no lightning in weeks, so there is no chance of sleepers (fires smoldering undetected for several days, then blowing up). All we need worry about, then, are human-caused fires. Say, how did the Eagle Bar Fire start?

Friday, September 2. Another eerie red sunrise. Following breakfast I chat with the I.C. (Incident Commander, i.e., the person in charge of all fire operations). He expects the fire eventually to burn 20,000 to 25,000 acres, much of it wilderness. The cost of the Eagle Bar Fire has now reached $4.8 million. Of that, $2 million is in suppression costs, billed (as required by law) to the person who started the fire; the remainder is the amount lost in property and timber damage.

Sunday, September 4. You can see fatigue on the firefighters' faces: they want out of here. Pounding line, inhaling large quantities of smoke and dust, has become mere drudgery. I too want the fire to be over, to be gone; the novelty of plentiful food and showers and meeting interesting people has long since worn off. I long for some solitude, a night of sleep without being troubled by generators. Hornets still ubiquitous.

While eating we're entertained by the zap! of bug-killers stationed strategically near the salad bar and serving trays. Very appetizing.

For entertainment I study the latest infra-red photographs. Fire now at 14,900 acres. Hey we're just about respectable, one of the Overhead Team jokes. That's total acreage within the perimeter of the fire, not actual burned acres. One can clearly see the mosaic of burn patterns along the ridges—how at its whim the fire has torched some swaths of trees but not others. And much of the burned acreage is also the result of backburning. Still, 15,000 acres is nothing to sneeze at.

The first clear indication that fire strategy, if not the fire, is winding down, comes today. Eight crews are to be demobilized.

Tuesday, September 6. The same day that two-thirds of camp will depart, a cold front with high winds is to pass over the region. Most of the crews and the entire Overhead Team break camp, load up in school buses, and head down the hill. Good riddance. I remain in the tower most of the day, avoiding good-byes, watching the queues of vehicles crawl down the mountain.

For the first time in weeks I can see distances of five, ten, then twenty miles as the front moves in, scouring the air clean and bringing with it row after row of cumulus clouds.

The fire seems unaware of the containment strategy planned for it. At dinner we're provided with yet one more awesome display, as the biggest column yet rolls out of Deep Creek, topping out at 15,000 feet, arcing all the way over to Smith Mountain as it's whipped by northwest winds.

Thursday, September 8. Sunny, cold and clear. The unmistakable feel of fall is in the air. Aspen leaves gilded, brush russett on the mountain slopes. Latest acreage on fire: 15,275. Actually it's doing exactly what the Overhead expected it to do: blow up in Deep Creek but eventually peter out as it moves higher into the patchy timber and rocky outcroppings of the wilderness. Latest rumor has it that what's left of camp will bug out on Saturday. Another cold front is expected to pass over that day, bringing with it snow.

Friday, September 9. I talk with Carol Ciliberti, a member of the Wasatch crew, about why she has chosen firefighting as a seasonal pastime. It has to do with the brute simplicity of the work, she explains, the simple yet physically challenging task of "pounding line" for twelve to fourteen hours, then seeing at the end of the day clear evidence of accomplishments. And the camaraderie that develops with the members of one's crew—the bonds that are formed between people who share the same brutal, dirty, and dangerous conditions.

Saturday, September 10. It's been three weeks since I reported the fire. "BRRR" is the operative word today: air temp at twenty-seven degrees, winds at more than 20 mph, wind chill minus four degrees. For the first time in months I fire up the woodstove. The morning weather report mentions snow levels dropping to 7,000 feet. "Lookouts should beware of winter-like conditions." Mercifully, the crews are not sent out on the line this morning.

In fact, they're not being sent out at all. They're being sent home! Or at least to another, hopefully, warmer fire. There is dancing in Horse Village today as eighty happy firefighters break camp. Within hours the tent-city disappears, leaving in its wake a dust bowl of trampled grasses.

And what about the fire? It still burns within Deep Creek, where it's supposed to burn. With the cold weather there's little chance for it to escape the wilderness. Millions spent on suppression, but the fire does its own thing anyway and will be suppressed, finally, only by snow and cold. Who ever said firefighting was an exact science.

Population of Horse Mountain returns to one. With snowflakes fluttering amidst the aspen leaves I go on one last long hike. Down through the meadows where I can wade once again through the chest-high tawny grass. Through the groves of spire-like subalpine fir. To return home in the dark, to enjoy once more and finally—for this is my penultimate day of the season—the delicious solitude of working a fire lookout.

The Lookout (1980s)

Doug Peacock

THE BUSHES PARTED and a chocolate brown grizzly stepped into the mountain clearing. Cautiously he ambled over the downed timber, swinging his huge dish-shaped face from side to side. He stopped. He stiffened and thrust his nose up into the cool evening air, reaching for a scent of the intruder. He reared, jaws agape, and slowly spun on his hind legs as if in a gentle dance. Suddenly he bolted down the mountain, through the basin, huffing and rolling over the deadfalls as easily as water cascading over rapids. His vast flanks rippled, disappearing as he reached the timber.

I watched from the ridge top on the spine of a tiny mountain range. This was only the beginning. It was the last of August, and within a week this Montana high country would be crawling with more grizzly bears than I could count.

Off to the southwest tall, anvil-shaped thunderheads rumbled. An electrical storm was heading my way. This naked ridge top was a poor place to be during a thunderstorm. I saw a distant flash of lightning and counted from the flash to the arrival of the sound: nearly twenty seconds, which meant that the storm was still about five miles away. Since I was more than an hour from the closest safe route off the top of the range, I knew I was going to get it.

I crammed my binoculars and notebooks into my small canvas pack and struck back up the ridge, striding along the game trail on the top of it. Behind me lightning struck. The interval between the flash and boom was now less than five seconds, and I needed to get off the treeless spine. Before me the ridge rolled up into a minor summit, then dropped off to the east. I picked a route below the top, contouring through the sidehill shrubfield—hardly an inviting bushwhack in the nearly impenetrable elk-high vegetation.

I dropped off the narrow ridge, sliding down the steep slope until I reached the highest stand of subalpine fir trees. A horizontal rain stung my face and neck. I dug a cheap green slicker out of the pack and squatted among the fir. The rain turned to hail. I shivered, then forgot about the cold as a lightning bolt exploded close by. A man standing on the ridge would be a lightning rod. I shrank even lower into the brush.

The bolts slammed into the mountain for ten minutes, then slacked off. The storm was moving on, though another was on the way. Soaking wet and cold, but still leery of walking the ridge top, I decided to continue contouring through the dense undergrowth along the side of the mountain, then down a spur ridge to the foot trail that led out. The brush was sopping, and every few minutes I slid a ways down the slick hillside. Nonetheless I made decent time, anxious to reach the relative security of the trail by dark.

Something made me freeze—maybe a scent, a subliminal sound. I listened. An animal was moving in the brush just ahead, about forty feet away. I may have made a bad mistake. Over the sound of the rustling underbrush I could clearly hear the breathing of a large animal. I had blundered onto a bedded bear, probably a grizzly. I did not understand why the animal did not charge or flee. I stood motionless for three minutes, watching the wind blow across the thick tangle of mountain ash and huckleberry, looking for some sign of the animal I could hear so clearly. Distant thunder rolled far to the west. My stomach knotted, but the initial sickly, panicky feeling at nearly stepping on a grizzly bear gave way to a growing confidence as I slowly comprehended that the bear neither feared me nor meant me harm. The invisible animal in the brush sounded lethargic, as grizzlies sometimes are when they retreat to day beds just before severe storms.

I slowly backed up the slope stopping every few seconds to listen for the bear, who seemed to be moving in the opposite direction. Although I usually talked to grizzlies when I accidentally stumbled on them, I was silent with this bear. We had just shared a lightning storm. Quiet was better.

In five minutes I reached the crest of the range again and moved rapidly northward, hoping to pass safely above the bear and drop down to the trail ahead of him. The hell with the approaching storm, I thought; I was less concerned with lightning at that point than I was about running into another grizzly.

The mountain crest rose to a small summit. I veered off and started down the open ridge, back to the trail, when the bear from the brush—

a medium-size light grizzly—burst into the open. The bear looked up at me, then turned and loped down the ridge, disappearing into the bushes again. It was a beautiful blond bear with ink-dipped forepaws and ears, a Siamese or panda color pattern not uncommon in this part of Montana, especially among younger animals.

I hurried down the side ridge, reaching the foot trail just as it began to rain again. The bear had vanished into the darkness, and I raced up the trail as fast as I dared, trusting my feet to find the dim but familiar path. Rounding the last corner on the trail, I saw a stark two-story pagoda, perched on a mountain top. At last.

I reached the foot of the lookout just at dark; the ridge carried more light than the gloomy north slopes of mountains. My fire lookout was a wooden structure built in the early thirties just after the forest fire of 1929. My twelve-foot-square living quarters were framed on all sides by glass windows and surrounded by a catwalk outside just high enough to be out of the reach of the tallest grizzly. It had been my summer home, my only home, since 1976.

I stumbled up the steps in the dark, glad to be home and happy to be living in the midst of a glut of grizzlies again. I stripped off my wet clothes and lit a Coleman lantern. A miniature wood stove sat in one corner with a prelaid fire ready to torch. I struck another match and lit it to take off the chill. Lightning flashed in the southern sky. This was a special night: the grizzlies had begun to gather in the high shrubfields of this small mountain range, and my real work was about to begin. Within a week, I would close up the lookout, sign off the government register, and drag my old movie camera up into the mountains, where I would spend the following weeks living with and filming bears at the Grizzly Hilton. Sometime in mid-September, the Black Grizzly would arrive and all hell would break loose. He was sufficiently big, cantankerous, and dominant to drive most other bears and myself out of the range. He charged animals almost reflexively. He was also my favorite bear, the paragon of grizzlies: a wild force, as indomitable and recalcitrant as the wind.

Meanwhile there was cause to celebrate. I dug under the army cot for a C-ration box. Inside were four good bottles of wine. I picked out the one I had in mind for welcoming the bears back—a 1970 Les Forts de Latour. I popped the cork and set the bottle near the stove to warm slightly, letting it breathe while I fixed a bisque of the wild chanterelle mushrooms I had picked under lodgepole pines on my last trip down the mountain. My tiny propane refrigerator was well stocked with necessary condiments—garlic, shallots, butter, limes, and canned milk. I could not believe the government paid me more than four dollars an hour eight hours a day to live up here. Like getting thrown into the briar patch. To the south a storm cell rained lightning on Teapot Mountain. I mechanically marked the strikes on my fire-finder map in the middle of the lookout. It was a bit late in a relatively wet year to worry about forest fires. The storm was headed my way, though, and would provide some dazzling pyrotechnics.

I poured a glass of wine and stepped over to an inexpensive portable tape recorder hooked up by phone wire to a series of "D" batteries taped to two parallel pieces of broken broomstick—my dork battery pack. Nosing the wine, I picked out and inserted a cassette, and the tiny glass house was filled with a Bach cello solo. Outside the lightning flashed and a drizzle of rain ran down the panes. The warmth of the wine and the fire rose to my head. By the third glass I was slightly giddy, a cheap drunk on an empty stomach. The stark music was punctuated by approaching booms of thunder. I felt like Captain Nemo in my mountaintop glass house. I whipped the flour into the butter, then stuck the roux in a 350-degree oven with a bay leaf to let it thicken. The wind gusted, the lanterns swung, and the entire wooden structure creaked and swayed in the wind. The aroma of freshly sauteed chanterelles filled the lookout. I poured another glass of wine. It was tough up here in the mountains.

The next morning I was beginning to pack up the lookout when I caught movement far down the slope east of the tower. Stepping out on the catwalk, I glassed the burned-over open hillside. A brown sow grizzly with two lighter cubs of the year moved rapidly and nervously across the exposed ground. The cubs had trouble keeping up. Sows with young were usually the wariest and shyest of other grizzlies, especially during a social gathering. The greatest danger to a young grizzly, excepting man, was another, larger bear, adult boars in particular.

The interactions in this seasonal congregation of grizzlies in prime huckleberry range were not as intense and frequent as those along salmon streams in Alaska. But this gathering was characterized by a dominance hierarchy in which only the largest males would cross an exposed patch of terrain with absolute security. You can tell where an animal fits into this social hierarchy by watching the way it moves, feeds, and plays. Body language allows bears to communicate their intentions and positions on the social hierarchy. I do not pretend to understand all of it. But the bears do; they all appear to know one another. Such behavior probably evolved through these gatherings for food.

The only species of animal that tries to get by in the wilderness without interspecific tact or communication is the human critter. All other animals take stock of what others do and make adjustments in their lives for the behavior and presence of the rest of the animal kingdom. Bears have a body language in which the mere style of gait communicates mood, aggressiveness, and even changes in season. A young brown bear on a salmon stream can tell at a glance if he should flee the big boar who is still 150 yards away. Elk know when grizzlies are predatory and when they can stand fifty feet away watching as a bear walks through the middle of their herd to the next berry patch.

Grizzlies communicate with their size, posture, mouths, ears, and eyes. A grizzly standing on its rear feet swinging its head is only trying to see and smell better. Bears *whoosh* when alarmed but are no threat to humans. A bear who *woofs* but does not run away is. If the grizzly opens and closes its jaw, and slobbers, it's time to leave. A grizzly with its head lowered near or across a forepaw and looking off to the side is indicating a willingness to move on peacefully if you do. If the bear's head is turned off to the side, you can still get out without getting chewed. Once the head is lowered straight on and the ears are flat back, you're probably going to get charged. If the eyes fix at the last moment and turn cold, you're in a world of shit. The icy stare is caused by the eyelids retracting to the corner of the eyes, revealing the yellow sclera. It happens only at the last second and is the final signal you'll see before flying fur.

The grizzly family hit the bottom of the open basin and followed a thin string of trees up the south side, where they rolled over the ridge to reach the safety of the timber that the 1967 forest fire had missed. The cubs wanted to stop and play. They started wrestling but were quickly left behind by their mother, who wanted no part of open ground during the middle of a hot day. Usually bears bed during the heat of these August days, but females with young can often be seen feeding or moving around.

These bears came from somewhere north of this small mountain range, perhaps from the Livingston Range of Glacier National Park or, less likely, from the Whitefish Range of Flathead National Forest. Precisely where they had spent their springs and summers I would never know. They came for the berries that grow here in reliable abundance. Huckleberries are the most important fruit, although bears also eat serviceberry, mountain ash, buffalo berry, hawthorn, and salmonberry. The key to great berry habitat is wildfire.

I moved a folding chair outside and sat shirtless in the warmth of the late summer sun. From this vantage point I had, in past seasons, seen as many as a dozen grizzlies a week moving into the range during late summer. The brown sow with her young cubs moved with purpose to a spot already picked out in the south of the range. Over the years, many generations of grizzlies had been introduced to this particular huckleberry habitat. Mothers brought their young as cubs and yearlings, who returned as subadults and then adult grizzlies, some with families of their own. In prime years, as many as a hundred grizzlies visited these mountains. One year I saw seventy-one different bears, a number subject to some degree of error since solitary grizzlies are difficult to tell apart but still one hell of a lot of bears.

From inside the lookout the radio growled. I turned up the volume and adjusted the squelch.

"730 Scalplock, 720 Control."

It was the first time in a month anybody except the Fire Cache had radioed me.

"This is 730 Scalplock, 720."

"730, your pack-out date is confirmed for September first. The mules will be up Friday. Also, be advised that Lisa will be hiking up tomorrow."

"Ten-four, 720. Thanks for the message. 730."

Despite all the years I had worked seasonally for the Park Service, I still found talking on the radio unnatural. I went back outside, leaned into the wind, and tried to regain my sense of solitude. Far below, a large dark hawk rode the currents blowing up the steep flanks of the mountain off the meandering channel of the Flathead River. I swung the glasses onto his slightly mottled deep brown back. An immature golden eagle. Good. I loved to look down on the backs of eagles. I flew with him for a while, effortlessly soaring over the fluted ridges and gullies. The Indians had called this summit Eagle Peak.

The day was hot for late summer. I was officially on duty looking for fires until four-thirty, but work was slow since the forests were soggy with heavy August rain. I decided to use up some of the precious water I had hoarded by filling garbage cans with snow and letting the sun melt it. Besides, grizzlies had the preeminent noses in the animal kingdom and Lisa was coming to visit. I needed a bath.

I stood naked on the catwalk and splashed water on my body from a tin wash basin sitting on the railing. The warm water ran off my toes and was blown away by the wind. The warmth of the sun and the chill of the wind made me feel exceptionally clean. I felt ready for anything. Tonight I would walk down the ridge again and look for bears in Sullivan Creek. Grizzly bears were arriving there daily now, and I would be looking for old acquaintances, especially the Black Grizzly, though I did not expect him to show up for another ten days or more. In the meantime I would close up the lookout, drop down off the mountain for a couple of days of serious sloth and bloat, check in with the boys at the Belton, and get ready to go up to the Grizzly Hilton and film bears with the Bolex.

A pair of kestrels hovered over the saddle just before Sullivan Creek, hanging nearly motionless in the late afternoon wind. I climbed the last rise and the whole of Sullivan Creek drainage opened up before me. The creek led out to a broad expanse of lodgepole, larch, and western white pine, which in turn swept back up onto the shoulders of the snowcapped Livingston Range twenty miles away. Beyond the Livingstons there are high basins and subalpine flats: the heart of Glacier National Park and prime summer grizzly habitat. Then there is another range with hanging glaciers and valleys that eventually drain onto the High Plains, which used to be buffalo country, wolf country, and the best griz country of all until we shot them all out in the 1880s.

Patches of the hundreds of square miles of uncut timber looked rusted in the oblique late summer sunlight. The blotches of off-colored orange lodgepole were caused by pine beetle, which had spread up the North Fork in epidemic proportions in recent years, probably precipitated by overprotection of forests from wildfire.

A dark, medium-size bear crossed an outcrop of rock on the opposite hillside. I brought up the binoculars and saw a good-sized black bear, *Ursus americanus,* sniffing the air and looking around. The bear was nervous about something. I was far away and across wind so I guessed that it was another bear. I glassed the slopes where the black bear semed to be looking. Nothing. Another ten minutes passed. The black bear, who had not moved, suddenly loped off toward the heavily timbered creek bottom. I caught a flash of silver among the berry brush. A small, light-colored grizzly walked out on a white windfall, leaning out to either side, stripping the berries from their bushes with its teeth. After a minute the bear was joined by an identical twin. The two looked yearling size. Sure enough, a great, blond head of a sow grizzly popped up above the brush thirty yards away.

The shadows lengthened. I had a good night. I started back along the trail to the lookout and rounded the corner where the lookout loomed against the purple sky. I paused at the bend, admiring the view, and heard rustling in the brush below the trail. Another bear. The place was already swarming with them. I quickly skirted on by, wondering what Lisa would run into. Probably not much during the middle of a warm day. She had spent more time with grizzlies than all but a handful of Montanans. Still, I found myself worrying. In about ten days, she would be beginning her eighth month of pregnancy and should start slowing down.

I lit two candles, whose flames wavered in the slight breath of wind that always found its way through the chinks in the lookout wall. It was amazing that the structure had withstood the full brunt of forty Montana winters with the loss of only one roof. To the south, I could see beyond Wild Horse Island to the far shore of Flathead Lake, a blue-gray plain in the fading light. To the north, the mountains of Canada were already hidden in the dark sky. A faint column of light shot vertically from the horizon: the aurora borealis. The northern lights would flash across the sky, throwing their luminous beams and curtains from the horizon to the heavens.

I had summered on that mountaintop for seven years. These past seven years, the grizzly years, had been a time of relative grace. I would not be coming back the following year. It was time to move on, time to leave these bears alone. I would go back up to the Grizzly Hilton one more time and wait for the Black Grizzly, then go where I could film a grizzly close up. Once that business was concluded it would be time to slack off, go to the Yellowstone country, fish and track a last bear to its den, then go south, Chihuahua maybe, look for the last Mexican grizzly and winter on the Sea of Cortés and the Piedras Negras desert. The following year I thought I might try the north country again: the Yukon or Alaska. All morning the radio had been squawking with cryptic messages. Someone had received puncture wounds on his chest and extremities. The Arrowroot drainage had been closed and armed rangers dispatched into the area. It was, no doubt, a bear incident, although the Park Service, like most insular agencies, was naturally paranoid about adverse publicity and tended to disguise their radio traffic in bureaucratese. The words *bear* or *mauling* were never mentioned. I would not find out what really happened until I came back to Syphilization and solicited the information at the Belton.

I was sitting at my table, bringing my notebooks up to date, when

I saw something white moving on the far hillside. Grabbing the binocks, I ran outside. On the distant trail, Lisa's big belly led her up the narrow trail through the brush; even at this distance the maternal waddle was distinctive. I raced off the mountain to meet her at the saddle and carry her pack up the last leg of the trail.

"Hi, baby," I said, grabbing her by both shoulders. We kissed. She was breathless, still gasping for air because of the three-thousand-foot climb and the child she was carrying. Beads of perspiration dotted her forehead. "Let me take your pack."

I lifted her Forest Service pack, surprisingly heavy with special treats and goodies for our last two days at the lookout. She managed a smile as we sat back on the edge of the trail while she caught her breath. "How was the hike up?" I finally asked.

"Okay," she said, taking my hand, "but I'm slowing down. This time up may be my last for a while. Don't worry, everything below is just fine. All the news is good."

I am one of those who, upon receiving a letter from an old friend, will skim it for bad news before reading it. My first concern was to know no calamity had taken place in the valley while I had been on my mountain.

"I saw bears," Lisa said. She meant grizzlies, of course. "They were in the last gully before the trees stop. I think the baby knew. It started kicking just as I spotted a straw-colored mom and two little cubs. She was very skittish and protective. She didn't see me, but she seemed to know something was wrong. The cubs kept rearing and trying to climb up on her back. They were awfully tiny. Like spring cubs. Just little balls of fur."

A gust of wind raised goose bumps on Lisa's slim, muscular legs. "Do you want to move on?" I asked. "You look cold."

"All right. Let's take it slow. It's good to be back up here."

We walked slowly up the ridge to the lookout, the gentle breeze blowing out Lisa's long hair on this warm, end-of-summer day. It was one of those rare mild days, everything important to me was near, I had no regrets and only a few lingering scores to settle.

We climbed up the steps of the tower and I closed the small gate that said PRIVATE QUARTERS. PLEASE KNOCK. Actually, visiting hikers were a rarity that late in the season, when the area had a good reputation for bad bears.

I fixed hot tea and opened a tin of smoked oysters. Lisa lay back on the cot while I started the first procedures of what would end up as

Montana Pizza later that night. We selected another bottle of my Bordeaux stash, a 1967 Chateau Margeaux, and let it warm to room temperature in the afternoon sun. I dug out my stethoscope from my green-beret medic days and a cloth measuring tape. I listened to the faint pulse of life: about 120 tiny beats per minute. I measured the distance from the top of her pelvic bone to the top of the uterus, 33 cm. She was right on schedule, two centimeters' growth since we had measured it two weeks ago. This was new business to me, having arrived rather late at parenthood.

I popped the cork on the wine. A chocolatey bouquet, big enough to fill the room, opened up. We toasted each other. Lisa had been many things to me, most important an ally, a friend and supporter in the endless skirmishes I fought around bears and wild country. I slurped a splash of wine out of Lisa's belly button, almost nonexistent now, for old times' sake. She napped in the sunlight pouring through the continuous ring of windows. I dug out the rest of the chanterelles and began cooking. The aroma of garlic, oregano, and basil blended with the Bordeaux. A pinch of sage, a little thyme. I loved cooking for people I liked in my lookout. The tower lent itself to certain indulgences as easily as it did austerity. Small celebrations of the flesh, like sharing food and drink—humble rituals performed before all the majesty and wildness of grizzly country—became religious moments. Or so it seemed as I poured the fourth glass of wine. Lisa's intake was limited to a glass per day. Splitting a bottle of wine with a pregnant woman was a deal.

By next morning we were in a cloud. Visibility was less than a hundred feet. I turned on the radio hoping to learn more about the bear mauling. The Arrowroot drainage was still closed and patrols were out, but beyond a few stark facts little information was transmitted. I worried about the Park Service overreacting. Usually, when someone was injured by a bear the area was closed and an attempt was made to trap or dispatch—bureaucratese for kill—the offending animal. It is nearly impossible, though, to be certain which bear is responsible. Bears, especially grizzlies, are on the move at that time of year. The upper Arrowroot drainage was, as far as I had been able to determine, emptied of bears by late summer. They had all come over to the lookout, and they had to pass the area where the National Park Service would be trapping or snaring, using smelly bait nearly irresistible to bears. Chances were they would snare the wrong grizzly.

We spent the day packing away the mundane articles that made this cold structure into a home every year. It was a melancholy time, since we assumed we would not return. The restricted vistas, the gray rim of lookout railing, the damp fog and surging light clouds reflected our mood. Darkness fell early under the clouds. We turned in, silent and downcast, and lit candles to illuminate the gloom.

The next morning the clouds had broken up. Far below, I saw the string of white packs on the backs of six mules led by a single horseman with a Moose River hat: it was Stu Sorenson, the packer. I stepped out on the porch to greet him.

"See any critters on the way up?"

"Saw a big brown grizzly in the first gully. He just stood there looking at me. The mules saw him first."

We unloaded the pack boxes. I helped as Stu tied in our gear with neat diamond hitches and reloaded the boxes.

"What're you going to do next, go down south?" asked Stu.

"Going to look for my favorite griz for a couple weeks, then go fly-fish the Madison and drop down to the Sonoran desert by Thanksgiving. Want to go to Mexico. Maybe go look for the last Mexican griz left back in the Sierra Madre. Keep hearing reports of tracks down there."

The pack string departed. We placed the shutter over the last exposed window for the winter and reluctantly followed the mules. At the switchback we paused, looking back at the tiny house on the mountaintop. It had been a good summer, but it was time to move on. The Grizzly Hilton awaited.

The Lookout D

R. Lightbulb Winders

THE HEAVY ODORS of bacon rind and pine needles linger in the door-way as Ranger Dick steps out to the platform. Cup of black coffee in hand, he breathes deep. Bluebirds sing. An expanse of virgin forest rolls out from the base of his twenty-foot tower. Ridge upon ridge of crack-ling dry pines stretch to a horizon of snowcapped peaks.

Ranger Dick raises the binoculars: No sign near the brook of the mama bear and her cubs. Not even a deer snitching hay from the corral by the tool cache.

Suddenly—he can almost smell it—he spots a column of smoke. That's from Gold Dust Creek! Near Charley Turner's cabin.

He slips into the building and cranks the telephone. A sleepy voice answers as Dick makes his short, urgent report. Then, in such haste that he forgets his brown ranger's hat, Dick races down the stairway to his horse. Shovel and ax strapped tight to his saddlebags, he gallops along the forest trails. Startled elk flee from his path.

Ranger Dick reaches Gold Dust Creek just as the Turner cabin bursts into flames. A body lies sprawled in the yard. It's Charley, dead with a bullet in his heart. But where is the prospector's young daughter, Mildred?

Ranger Dick grabs his ax, darts to the blazing cabin, and chops through the door in four mighty blows. He rushes inside. Mildred lies tied and gagged in the corner, entrapped by a crescent of fire. Tongues of flame lap at her cascading golden locks. Choking and smoke-blinded, Ranger Dick enters the curtain of fire, lifts Mildred like a rag doll, and stumbles out of the burning building.

By now fire has spread to the timber. But fifty firm-jawed rangers have already appeared. Swinging axes and shovels, they valiantly fight the blaze.

Dick loosens Mildred's gag. "Dan McGraw," she gasps, "upstream, with Papa's gold." Then she faints.

Ranger Dick jumps back into the saddle and spurs his steed. Faster than lightning he speeds through the wood in pursuit of the vile Dan McGraw.

A glimpse of red bandanna through dark branches. In another moment our hero has reached the villain. He leaps from his horse and knocks Dangerous Dan to the ground.

Fist against fist; blow against blow; it's a life-and-death struggle as the two men roll through the underbrush. Smoke thickens on all sides as both gasp for air. Dan sneers, kicks the ranger in the groin, and rises to flee. Flames crackle in the trees overhead.

Shirt torn, knuckles bloodied, Dick struggles to his feet.

With a cougarlike pounce he's on the scoundrel. Grasping the dastardly villain's shoulder, he knocks him flat with a single well-aimed blow. Dan lies motionless in the yellow grass.

The inferno is upon them. Without a second to lose, Ranger Dick snatches the pouch of gold from Dan's belt, leaps onto his horse, and rides away. Glancing back, he sees a pillar of raging fire. The villain has received his due.

Ranger Dick gallops to the gutted Turner cabin. While rangers scrape charred logs on the edge of the clearing, he bends low to Mildred. Her faint breath quickens; her eyes flutter back to life.

As they ride back to the lookout tower, he holds her firmly in his arms. Her yellow hair is like silk against his callused hand. She gazes sweetly at his rugged face. She says, "I love you, oh hero of the woods."

. . . Nowadays, as the sun tops the snow white peaks, Ranger Dick splits the kindling; Mildred bakes the biscuits. Together they live in the little brown tower, happily ever after.

A fire lookout is a building. A fire lookout is a person who lives in the building. It's as simple and confusing as that.

I don't remember when I first learned of either of them, the man or his tower. The neolithic fog of childhood memory has swallowed that earliest revelation. It certainly wasn't from direct experience; not when I spent my early years in the Midwest. From the archetypal romance I associate with fire lookouts, I rather think Hopalong Cassidy had something to do with it, or even Walt Disney. It certainly dates back to days before I knew the names Jack Kerouac and Gary Snyder.

The first lookout building I ever saw was on Black Mountain in the

Wyoming Bighorns. It was June. I was amazed to find snow on the trail, and I was disappointed to find the building uninhabited. "Is it deserted?" my hiking buddy and I wondered. The door was locked. "Maybe he's gone to town for the day."

Putting a lookout on top of Black Mountain seemed an unfortunate afterthought, for an old forest fire had left nothing but charred snags and scarred scenery. The air was chill; storm clouds gathered. I peeked through the glass panes. There was a stack of Bighorn National Forest maps on the counter. On the covers I could see a list of animals—moose and elk and mountain lion. "Just think," I said in awe, "the ranger gets to see all those wild animals."

I hiked to my second lookout two weeks later, on Mount Washburn in Yellowstone National Park. After an arduous four-mile climb to the top, I was crestfallen to discover we could just as easily have driven a paved road that led to the door. A cold wind blew sleet at us; we hid inside a little room in the tower's concrete base along with several other hikers, who carried whistles and wore Christmas bells to chase grizzly bears away.

The ranger, the first lookout I ever saw in the flesh, entered from the storm with a sour don't-talk-to-me frown and climbed the stairs to the glass room, closing the door behind him. I kept waiting for him to come back and invite us up to see the view. But he remained aloof in that cabin of glass where the magic of being a lookout takes place.

The romance of being a lookout took hold of me that summer. But the dream seemed so unattainable that it was years before I dared apply for the job. In the meantime I'd read Snyder and Kerouac and discovered an attitude toward mountaintop living more profound than heroic rescues and wild deer. Ranger Dick had become a Buddhist monk with a zenny sense of humor, a mystic who sought alpine solitude as a means to *satori*.

It was through a slim but influential literary tradition about Northwest fire lookouts that I first learned of Washington's North Cascades. Gary Snyder, in particular, became a prototype for the back-to-nature longhairs of the sixties and seventies like myself. His interest in oriental thought and ecological balance presaged much of the thinking that, once considered antithetical to the American Ideal, has in recent years become an integral part of our society. Kerouac's description of Snyder in *The Dharma Bums* and the poet's own journal of being a lookout on Sourdough Mountain in *Earth House Hold* made me want to be *just like Gary Snyder.*

I thought of all that a few days back as I sat in the little cliff-flanked yard of Green Mountain lookout. Now that I was a full-fledged lookout, I had no need for prototypes. Mountaintop living, like any other kind of living, has a way of rearranging aspirations in unforeseen ways.

It was one of those Parnassian Indian summer days when the sky is finally clear after a chilly spell of rain. Sprawled out on dirt and rock, soaking in sunlight like a doughnut sucks up coffee, I studied the mountains through binoculars for the five-hundredth time, tracing ragged ridge lines and descending chasmed waterfalls. Then, leaning back over a rock, I looked at the mountains in a new way—upside down. They suddenly seemed faded, alien, and small. So I gave them a friendly wink, then let my gaze slowly drift toward the sun, traveling across fading grades of blue to a meridian that glared like a spaceship hull, molybdenum alloy reflecting foreign starlight.

This must be what being a lookout's all about, I thought, the chance to see life from a different angle.

In fact, it's not just having the opportunity for fresh perception that makes mountaintop living special. We all have those opportunities each moment of our life. As a lookout, however, I'm forced to see things differently. Cut off from the distractions and noise, I'm compelled to gaze upon my immediate environment. With an empty appointment book, I must make up new rules for spending each day.

Not everyone thinks a lookout vocation worthwhile. After all, a man my age should be settling into a career and making money. I suppose it all comes down to a question of values. I could be bouncing through the desert in a new four-wheel-drive jeep or attending the season's opening of the San Francisco opera, but I'd rather watch the shadows move across Downy Creek's thick virgin forest. I could get a job on a road construction crew, tearing up countryside so people could reach L.A. from Seattle four hours faster. Or I could make it a point to drink the finest imported French wine each night. But I'd rather sprawl in the mountaintop sun, dwarfed by the silence of the Glacier Peak Wilderness.

Being a lookout is also a matter of personal survival. The fire watch isn't apt to succumb to ulcers, chronic anxiety, high blood pressure caused by gluttony, or the poisons that engulf our communities—petrol fumes, cigarette smoke, asbestos dust, stray bullets, and the like. Better yet, the lookout may even develop immunity to that most fearsome pathological condition—the drive for prestige and wealth. It seems quite odd that my compatriots conspire to kill themselves by binges of overeating and spasms of overachievement.

But the lookout also has a real role to play, one that justifies the salary. It's a role that has its roots in our most primitive fears—fear of wild nature, fear of the known and unknown dangers that lurk there. The lookout's express purpose is to guard us from wild, elemental fire. He, or very likely she, also keeps an eye open for violent weather, helps rescue climbers who have been thrown down by unfriendly mountains, and counsels hunters who have been driven mad by inner darkness.

The lookout is a link between forgotten nature and twentieth-century man: keeper of the forest, guardian of the trees, who with watchful eye and magic spells strives to keep them standing. The lookout acts as buffer between valleys of giant trees and bureaucrats with their heads full of finances, logging targets, and political expediency. The lookout understands firsthand what wilderness is and why we should cherish it. To perform this task competently, the lookout must settle in a house on the borderland and dissociate self from societal time. The lookout's duty is to slow down the murderous pace of our American civilization, to look down at civilization's actions from raw nature's position, to ruminate and drag feet, to make certain that change doesn't happen at a thoughtless pace. *Crash! Krunkle-krunkle!*

I ran into the lookout. Some damn ground squirrel had been rifling my food stores.

Rapid skittering, followed by my shouting. The ground squirrel scurried under the bed and hid in a stack of planking. I poked a broom between the boards until the critter scuttered toward the door. Shouting imprecations, I chased him down the catwalk, hell-bent on cracking his spine. But he slipped in a crack beneath a rock.

I stomped back to the door and slammed it shut. The cheek of that beastie! Leaning against the splintered rail, I looked back at the jagged skyline, searching for the thread of thought I had been following but a moment before.

But the mountains wore a haggard look. My thoughts turned to survival, to the rivalry between beasts and humans for nature's larder. I began to scan the forest for a stray whiff of smoke. After all, that was my duty.

I'd awakened from the lookout's dream and entered the lookout's time of watchfulness. Balancing the dream and the reality—that's the true work of life. There was no fair maid languishing in the valley for my aid. The hills and forests flattened beneath a bulldozer blade whether it was I who drove the machine or not. In my quest for a dream, I'd found instead a need to keep my eyes open wide. I'd embraced the vocation of lookout—the job of looking, looking until eye and mind came together in clear sight.

Ground Squirrel

MARTHA HARDY

THE HAWK HAD NOT come back. The sky had been empty since two hours before, when the shadow of death fell from it upon Tatoosh. There was not even a breeze in the wide, still afternoon. Outside the north windows, the flowers blooming beside the trail to the tool shelter had quietly turned to the west, their bright eyes following the sun. No sleek shape of a ground squirrel darted along the path among them, creating a tiny wind by the swiftness of his passing. Only the bees and flies were abroad, the bees hovering above the flowers, the flies swarming below the shutters.

There were flies inside the house too, buzzing out the last of their brief lives against the warm west panes. I unlatched the corner window and swung it open. When I had coaxed the last stubborn horsefly to freedom, the afternoon was as silent as it was motionless. I got out the Lookout's diary to record the day up to this hour. August 4, clear, warm, calm, a perfect day in the late spring of Tatoosh, a season of such loveliness that each day's entries should have been a poem. But there was nothing pleasant about this day's record.

6:00—Woke up, got up, check looked. Sat on steps and fed Impie graham crackers.

7:00—Got breakfast, started "dollar" cookies for squirrel.

8:00—Called Packwood, told Betty about Impie and the crackers. She said she would like to see him.

9:00—Saw hawk hanging over Muddy Fork basin.

10:00—Gave Impie half his cookies. Hid some under shale and watched him dig for them.

11:00—Lunch, ten-minute nap.

1:00—Called Packwood. Told Betty about Impie's excitement over

159

his cookies. She told Zelma and Bill. Bill said to tell the schoolma'am that her boy friend Spunky is famous in Packwood.

2:15—Split wood, carried snow, watched hawk, gathered rocks in pile to throw if he came too close. Impie out of sight as usual during early afternoon.

2:45—Bill called to ask if I saw a smoke at mouth of Coal Creek, reported by Pompey. Looked carefully, reported no smoke, only bright reflection on gray water at mouth of creek. While talking, saw Impie being silly, as often, before starting p.m. chores. Large shadow crossed yard. Heard whistle of fright. Bill was saying take reading on bright spot, so he could plot it and compare with Pompey report. Saw shadow of hawk as he flew away. Took reading for Bill, phoned it in. Looked for Impie. Couldn't find him.

3:15—Bill called, said my reading and Pompey's crossed near mouth of creek, so smoke was bright spot, but he sent Willie to check anyhow. I told him about hawk and Impie. He said hawks are good dive bombers, and Spunky may be gone.

4:45—Called Packwood. Betty asked if I'd seen Impie. I said no, and she asked me to call if he showed up.

I closed the diary and looked out for the hundredth time in the last two hours, hoping to see Impie racing up the path. It was the height of his afternoon feeding time, and he should have been tearing back and forth, face big with crackers, cookie, pancake, then empty and pointed eagerly for more.

Outside I called and called, but only the murmur of Butter Creek answered. Sitting on the steps, I looked at Mount Rainier. Softly white it gleamed and its rocks were palest violet. It looked remote and unapproachable. There had been other times when it had seemed close enough for me to touch it by merely holding out my hand. But now, when my need was great, its soul had withdrawn into some secret inner place. Although its planes and angles were blended into an aspect of perfect peace and the sunlight was laying long, supple shadows across it from west to east, there was no comfort in it.

Walking down to the tool shelter, I looked at Impie's well-defined path in the trail. The flat place between woodpile and shed was feathered with his tracks. In front of the door was a pattern of little skiddy places where he had slid to a stop before turning sharply up the bank to his burrow. I climbed the bank and stood looking down into his hole.

On the cliff nearby, a rock began to roll toward the lake, making a lost sound.

Back in the house, I took out the "Log of Impie" which I had been keeping since my third day here. It was not a log of Impie alone, but of all the birds and animals I had seen on Tatoosh. I had named it for him because he had become the leading man, the featured player in the drama of wild life going on around the station. I did not feel as if I ever wanted to write in it again. But because I had kept it accurately and because it was an honest biography of one of the most vibrant creatures I had ever been privileged to know, it seemed a shame not to complete the record. I opened the notebook to a fresh page.

Outside near the steps, shale rattled, but it was merely juncos hopping on the rocks, looking for a bedtime snack of oats. There was only one cup of rolled oats left in the big round box, and I wondered if I should keep it for their breakfast. They were making such urgent twittering that I thought of crumbling the rest of Impie's little cookies, but put the idea away. Tomorrow would be time enough to give them the cookies.

I went back to the log, but not to write in it. Instead I sat staring south, where Hood was a lonely phantom, and thought about that rascal Impie. He had certainly been thrilled about his first cookie. I had put it under a piece of shale, leaving merely an edge showing because he seemed to enjoy digging for his loot.

When he found it he tried to reach under and nip it out. When that did not work, he laid his ears back and straddled the shale, a fair-sized piece larger than he was. Lying flat, hind feet braced on each side against the ground, front paws holding the shale under his chin, he gave a violent shove. The rock shot back under his belly, where he kicked it away. Then having snatched the cookie in both hands, he whirled and looked up as if to say, "Powerful, ain't I?"

It was time to start writing. But before I began what was doubtless the last chapter, I wanted to sit in the waning light and read what I had already written. Because, until I made the final entry, I could still pretend that Impie might come back, bouncing up the steps, his eyes eager.

There was nothing about him on the first day, Monday, July 12, but a hawk was entered. On the trip to the top, as the packstring came out of the timber into sight of Tatoosh, I had seen a bird hanging motionless above the snowy slopes, so perfectly synchronized with the wildness of the scene that its presence there had seemed inevitable. When I asked Al if it was a hawk or an eagle, he answered, "You'll see plenty of both, but that's a big hawk looking for fresh meat for dinner."

Tuesday, July 13. Saw the hawk again today in the west, with morning sun full on him. First he hung motionless, then fluttered, then hung still again, sweeping wings curved up at the tips. An hour later when I was standing on the snow, check looking south, some impulse made me turn around. Out of the north, from the direction of the jagged wall beyond the little lake, came a hawk, headed straight toward me, exactly on my eye level. On he came till I could see, or imagined I could, the intent expression of his eyes. I was getting ready to duck when he swooped up and missed my head by inches.

Wednesday, July 14. No wild life, too foggy. Lonesome, too. A pet would surely come in handy.

Thursday, July 15. At dawn a buck walked by the house, and a ground squirrel came to get some pancakes. Saw a chipmunk, too, much smaller than the squirrel. The squirrel was brown with two stripes, one light, one dark, on each side; the chipmunk grayish tan, with many stripes, even on his face. At a guess, the munk was about half the size of the squirrel.

Friday, July 16. Chipmunk on rockpile by telephone switch pole, hugging his little bosom. The squirrel appeared, raced over the snow, disappeared over the cliff. Reappeared on phone rockpile, holding paws delicately before his nose, as he watched the house. Came again at dusk, running across the drift as if showing off, snow flying back under his heels.

Saturday, July 17. This morning there were large three-toed tracks on the path from the tool shelter. Bill said cougar tracks! Asked if I'm going to tame it. I said no, a squirrel's big enough for me.

Sunday, July 18. Sitting outdoors to watch the squirrel, with flies, skeeters, gnats all having themselves a big Sunday dinner off me. Butterflies all over the place, very gay. This morning as I opened the door, a creature that must have been a marmot ran along the apron north of the house and disappeared down the west slope. Larger than a rabbit, it had woolly, two-toned fur, a fat tail, and a clumsy run. Marmots, according to Bill, are related to squirrels and chipmunks. This afternoon the marmots are whistling from their stronghold in the west, where I think they live in the great boulders broken from the west face of the peak.

Indoors. Just made a dramatic rescue. Was sitting here, safe from bugs, writing, when I heard some "plunkety" splashes. Listened, more splashes. Looked in water can on stove, nothing there. Then to door, and there, swimming frantically from side to side of the water tub, and pawing at the slippery sides with his little claws, was a chipmunk. At sight of me he did not know whether to be glad or sorry, but when I put my hand under him, he stopped struggling, leaped, and landed square in the other tub. Took my second offer eagerly and jumped to a rock to squat till he got his breath. Then with a shake he vanished around the house, his tail a skinny stick. Now there's a bare branch in each tub for him to climb out on if he tries another bath.

Monday, July 19. This morning I saw a pretty sight—the ground squirrel sitting in the early sunshine on top of a silvery stump. There he loafed, tail curled under, front paws tucked away like a cat's, eyes blinking. I was glad, because he seems to have so little time free from uneasiness.

When I was eating my breakfast of ham and hotcakes, he was outside the house, looking up, sniffing. When I threw him some rolled oats, he ducked under the rockpile, but the oats disappeared while I was washing dishes. Then I heard rocks rattling by the phone post and saw the squirrel excavating, so intent on his work that I got my first chance to inspect him closely.

He has fine, thick, smooth fur, with a tinge of cinnamon over the brown, one seal and one tan stripe on each side of his back, the light above the dark. As he digs, he holds his ears back in little pointed loops and makes the dirt fly.

Tuesday, July 20. The squirrel's technique in getting oats from under shale is an example of determination. He tackles rocks a foot long, though he himself is not over five or six inches from tip of nose to base of tail. There is a certain greediness in his behavior that is not altogether lovely. But who am I to criticize a chap who has to get his winter supplies the hard way?

Once while digging he seemed to sense that I was looking out the window, because he sat up, studied my face until apparently satisfied, and went back to his work.

Having exhausted the possibilities of the spot beside the steps, he spent the next half-hour in front of the tool shelter, snooping in bare earth. There was something almost reptilian in his litheness as he crawled around on his belly. His body rippled and swayed, whereas it usually flashes and darts.

While this was going on, two chipmunks appeared near the door-step. When I went out for a check look they ran, but when I came back they were at the steps again and made a dive for the house. Finding no opening in the shale foundation, they paused for a second of panic, then ran frantically around the corner. Knowing what a spot they would be in if a hawk should attack them near the house, I went around the building moving shale to make four or five holes on each side. When I returned to the door, there was a chipmunk making prompt use of a hole.

Wednesday, July 21. Sitting on the steps tonight, I saw the squirrel appear on the snow of the east shoulder. He sat up high, looked my way, came leaping in great arcs toward the house, dashed directly to the rock platform on which my feet were resting, and sat there not six inches from my toes. His eyes were brilliant with excitement, his ears erect, his fur a dream of sveltness, his tail a whole vocabulary of curios-ity and daring. He was a magnificent little devil.

Suddenly he dropped to all fours and sauntered to the oats, ignor-ing me. When I got up and came in the house, he didn't budge, and when I returned and sat down, he took a few more kernels. Then he looked up, decided my expression had taken a turn for the worse, and dived for a hole under the house.

Thursday, July 22. Wonder what the ground squirrel does when it storms. If he's male, he probably just burrows deeper into his nest, and says with true masculine bravado, "Let 'er rip!"

Friday, July 23. Saw three hawks today, in a trio of gliding flight over the basin of Butter Creek. I turned away for a moment, then looked back, but they were gone—where, I could not imagine. There is something almost ominous about these hawks.

The ground squirrel let me watch him wash his face today. Sat on long hind feet, put his front paws together one over the other, rubbed vigorously across nose, eyes, cheeks, chin. With each hand separately he scrubbed earnestly behind his ears.

He has strong supple hands and feet. On his feet are five slender dark brown toes, the inside digit resembling a thumb. On his hands are four fingers and a nubbin thumb. The backs of hands and feet are a rich tan like his belly. Many shades of brown, tan, russet are mingled on his fur. As light strikes him at different angles it reveals the various hues and tones.

He appeared just now from an unusual direction, around the southeast corner of the house, and found me on the step. I must have looked more formidable from that angle, because he stopped, retreated, sallied forward, retreated, advanced, backed up. Finally with an angry jerk of the tail, he was gone. But he soon came back along the north, slipped to the oats, grabbed a mouthful. Then he sat up and gave me a long, intense inspection. At last, as if to express his decision, he lifted one forepaw from its position with the other under his chin, and held it out. If I had not already succumbed to his charm, this would have finished me.

Saturday, July 24. Named the squirrel today, "Impie." Found an entrance to his burrow on the edge of the cliff beside the tool shelter in a clump of red heather. He must have a second entrance under the building, because he often disappears there. But usually he follows the path to the tool shelter, then darts at right angles up the bank. It's his habit to stop twice on the way, once by the lumberpile, once by the woodpile, to glance at the sky. The hawks have been over the house so much lately that I wonder that he has the courage to stay in the open at all. He's wary, but I'm afraid that some day he'll forget.

Sunday, July 25. Home after almost sitting on a bear. The squirrel has been gathering load after load of oats. He has become so excited about the big heaps I've been putting out that he has eliminated his stops by wood- and lumber-piles. Starting from the door he gains so much momentum going downhill that it is all he can do to stop when he reaches the tool shelter. When he puts on the brakes, the dirt flies. Then he makes one long leap up the bank and dives head first into the heather.

He has been gobbling so fast in the last few minutes that his mouth must feel like a hot-box. He leaped toward a tub, peered up at the rim, stepped a few inches to one side where the rocks were higher, jumped to the edge of the tub and clung there, head down, holding by his hind feet. The surface was about eight inches from the top of the tub, but that did not bother stretchy old Impie. He got his mouth down and began to lap like a cat, filling the tub with big ripples till one bounced back, went up his nose and made him sneeze.

His feeding methods are comical. Having uncovered a rich cache, he takes about two-thirds of it, then tires of the spot and leaves it to gather bits here and there. However, he seems to remember the places he has left and comes back to clean them up.

He is certainly a sight with a full load in his cheeks. His face gets as broad as his body, till his mouth looks like a kewpie's. A bad case of the mumps cannot compare with Impie when he gets his face full.

Monday, July 26. I'm resting my bruises from hanging the phone line, and giving myself time to study Impie, who now gathers food by the steps without hesitation. I come and go, move quickly, speak to him, but he feeds without batting an eye.

I think perhaps he likes me now, feeling a little as I do, that companionship is something to be prized even if with another sort of being. I'm not convinced that all he wants is food, because if it is, why does he stop feeding to look at me with a winsome tilt of the head and a gentle expression? When he first arrives at the step, morning and afternoon, he is frankly concerned with nothing but loot, but after he has taken home a dozen loads, the avid expression seems to fade and be replaced with a certain gentleness.

While I was out check looking once today, he got in the house, and when I entered, his curiosity turned to panic. He tried to claw his way out through the panes, and when I shut the door, intending to coax him out of his fright, he hid under the bunk and wouldn't budge. I began to picture him dead from heart failure and opened the door to let him sneak out. The episode didn't bother him much, because five minutes later he was cantering past with a faceful of dry grass.

Tuesday, July 27. This afternoon Impie has been a regular scatter-brain, touched off by the misty weather. He came to the house, jumped on the apron, looked up at the window to see if I was watching, then bounced to the edge of the cliff and onto the little bench which Al built. I call it "Impie's bench" because he likes it, and now he posed on it, looking off toward Mount Rainier like a little tourist. Then he dropped to his belly, flopped to his side, leaped up, did a whiligig dance, and jumped down. Having whizzed to the tool shelter where he tried to climb the door, he took a quick bath in the damp earth, rolling over and over. Dug a hole, sat in it, tried to climb the door again, ran up the path and made a flying leap to the top of the cooler. On the catwalk he flipped rocks with his nose, ran at a chipmunk, turned his back and sauntered off to the phone rockpile, where he crouched in the wind, soft hair blowing.

Wednesday, July 28. I am lonesome tonight and wish Impie were in the house with me. Elmer called and asked if I had gone crazy yet like a sheepherder, trying to tell which is the long way of the quilt. No, I said, but almost, trying to tell which side of the glass to drink from. That's a shame, said Elmer, now tell me the latest about my rival. That'll take your mind off your troubles.

He likes to turn over rocks, I said. Ah, said Elmer, just like me, always waiting with bated breath to see what will be under the rock of fate when the new day turns it over.

You have one thing in common, I said, inflated egos. There you do us wrong, he protested. That's just an act. Well, I said, I'll admit Impie puts on an act. The Stripes (the chipmunks because they have so many of 'em) seem to know this. They come sneaking to the feed-pile and sniff the tip of Impie's tail. When he jumps at 'em they scamper off, but when he goes back to his oats, they sniff again. That game goes on for an hour at a time. He's twice as big as they are, but he's no bully. Hum, said Elmer. You're getting too fond of that squirrel. I'm jealous.

Thursday, July 29. Al and Carl have gone to bed, so I'll take a few minutes to put down the new squirrel, Rusty. This morning I saw what I thought was Impie in front of the house, digging under some pretty little saxifrage plants. Dig, dig, dig, jump! Dig, dig, dig, jump! Impie, I thought, more addlepated than ever. Then the furry bit came bounding up to the phone rockpile, and I saw that it wasn't Impie at all, because it was redder and had a skimpy tail. Hearing a rattle north of the house, I looked out, and there was Impie himself. He dived under the building, came out on the rockpile and made a jump for Rusty. Around and around the water tubs they went, then streaked downhill, leaving me to wonder whether Rusty's a boy or a girl, aspirant to the throne of Tatoosh or potential power behind it.

Saturday, July 31. Rusty's back. He sneaks to the feed-pile and gobbles with a worried look till Impie starts for him. Now Rusty dodges while his pursuer hurtles past, managing a change of direction barely in time to see which way Rusty went. When Rusty has safely run off, Impie sits on a rock and says bad things through his nose.

There's no doubt that he considers the house and premises his private property, to be shared with the juncos and the Stripes but not to be trespassed on by another ground squirrel. However, he, Rusty and the Stripes all have an understanding about hawks and warned each other today when two hawks showed up.

In perfect unison the two were weaving a superb pattern of flight, gliding, banking, fluttering, swooping. When one beat the air with a single stroke, so did the other. When one perched in a tree, the other perched on another branch in the same tree. When one went into a great spiral, the other was its shadow.

Then one came to sit on the hitching rail now emerging from the snow. Impie vanished, the Stripes scattered, Rusty dived for a hole. Later, when a baby junco fluttered around a corner, Impie fled under the house. Once, in a moment of blind panic for no reason that I could see, he made a plunge for safety, clattering into a rock and dazing himself. Having crawled to the doorstep, he crouched at my feet, his body vibrating to the thump of his heart, his ears laid flat, his lips trembling. He's a brave boy, though, because he was soon back at the oat pile.

At least one of the hawks knows the location of his burrow, because after the other had disappeared, it flew to within a foot of the hole. I dashed out, but before I could grab for a rock the hawk was gone.

Sunday, August 1. How fast the Stripes run! They almost fly. Impie and Rusty are lively enough, given to amazing leaps, but the Stripes are not earthbound at all. They come soaring in from the shale shoulder like tiny gray planes wearing the brown and white emblems of some mysterious little kingdom tucked away in the rocks.

One of them got so excited at the feed-pile today that he didn't know what he was doing. Having crammed his face, he was suddenly overwhelmed with impatience to bury that load and gobble another. He backed up a few feet, scrabbled in the shale, disgorged his little faceful, slapped the earth down with such rapid motions of his front paws that they were a blur, and flew back to the feed-pile.

He took his next load past the hitching rail onto a big rock at the edge of the cliff, where he sat twitching his straight-up tail so fast that all I could see was a haze of nervous impatience. It doesn't take much to fill the tiny pointed face of a Stripe. About six bites and his cheeks pooch out.

Once today Impie showed up at the corner of the catwalk gathering a mouthful of dry grass. First he pushed it into shape with his paws, taking care to have no dangling ends, then hurried home, pausing at his door as if to make sure no enemy was looking before he slipped in with his little bale of hay. I saw him later with both moss and grass, when he didn't care how much like a hayseed he looked and ran home with his load trailing between his front legs. His inconsistency seemed odd until I remembered my own. The more I see of Impie the better I realize that ground-squirrel behavior looks pretty good compared with human. I think he could kill Rusty if he chose, but he merely runs him away and sometimes even tolerates him with an air of, oh well, I have lots, why shouldn't you have some?

Monday, August 2. Impie certainly has a bag of tricks. After I'd finished baking today, I put three pans out to soak, one with biscuit dough around the edge, the second with cookie batter, and the third with remnants of stewed apricot. After the snow melted in them, they all held murky water, and in the cookie pan was a cup with batter thick on the rim. Looking out, I saw Impie, front feet on the cup, hind feet on the pan, nibbling the cup. He then cleaned the pan, ate some apricot, and had a long cool drink of cookie water. He finished his meal with all four feet on the rim of the biscuit pan, drinking water and eating biscuit dough.

Then he jumped down, gave the pans a look as if to say thanks, stretched, belly to ground, torso swaybacked, and scampered to his bench where he sat washing his face and grinning with satisfaction.

A hawk hung over Tatoosh today, high, high up in the mist, the very spirit of things untamed, both beautiful and frightening.

Tuesday, August 3. Today is the day! Impie ate out of my hand and came in to explore the house. I was sitting on the step holding a piece of graham cracker when the big event took place. He was mooching around my feet, gathering bits and eying the big brown fragment in my fingers. Then he crept up, gently helped himself to the cracker and started home like a flash, shocked at his own daring.

From then on it was simple. Those crispy squares got him. He was still cagey about it, though, filling his cheeks with broken pieces first. He'd get his face wide and lumpy-looking before he would come to my hand, seeming to feel that since he had to run after taking the big piece, he might as well run with a full cargo.

When Rusty edged in and stole a stray bit, Impie gave chase, holding a piece in one paw. When he came back he still had it, but how he did it I can't imagine. Then Rusty was so foolish as to bury a piece in full sight of Impie, who promptly dug it up and actually swallowed it, as if to say, "That's what happens when you steal stuff and bury it under my nose. It goes where you won't ever get it."

The first time I offered him a whole cracker I didn't think he would try to carry it. He took it politely, without snatching, selected the proper side to put in his mouth, pushed it way back and started home with the cracker dragging to his toes. But when he got to his hole he had a problem to solve that would have impressed even the "Professor": How to get that big brittle cracker into a three-inch opening and around a bend without breaking it.

Sitting on his haunches, he turned the cracker around and around until he must have decided to bull his way in. Giving a resolute shove, he vanished, cracker and all. Next I tried him with two squares fastened together, saying to myself, here's the problem that's really going to stump him. He eyed the huge offering thoughtfully, then took it by the long side and started home with a wing of cracker protruding beyond each ear.

He made the trip at a heavy lope, squatted by his hole, turned the cracker to the short side, and shoved it down. I wish I had a periscope to look into his burrow. Does he stack the crackers on top of each other, or break them up and stomp them down? And what will he do when they get soggy and start to mold? There are certainly a lot of simple mysteries I'll never solve unless I am reincarnated as a ground squirrel.

Late in the afternoon a hawk hung like the shadow of death over the marmot country, watching, waiting. Shrill warnings came from a marmot sentry, then silence, while the hawk flew away over the canyon of Butter Creek where the shadows of evening had gathered.

That was the end of yesterday. I closed the book and pushed it away. There in its pages was Impie, saucy and bad, beloved and good, courageous, impetuous, daring. Let him alone, living and vibrant, I told myself. Don't write him down as dead. What happened today, August 4, I will never forget, and by shutting the book I might keep the life of Impie warm between the covers.

Low in the west the sky was a clear pale blue, crossed by limpid stripes of that yellow-green which is never seen except in the sky at evening. Across the sun lay a finger of gold, and over Saint Helens a rosy angel hovered. Far-off ranges were all in gray, nearer ones in lavender. On the snow of the northwest ridge lay a pattern of lilac shadows, and the drift at the edge was a curve of white and blue. As the gold across the sun darkened to rust, a junco twittered among the firs.

I got into bed while a tender color still filled the room. Drifting toward sleep I wondered vaguely about the incomprehensible value of life. It must be a big thing, life, the life of a squirrel, or a tree, or a human being. Even the life of a hawk.

At dawn I woke with a sense of something sad just beyond the threshold of memory. Then I remembered, and lay watching the sunrise, wondering if in some distant heaven Impie might be waking to a dawn far lovelier than this. A sheaf of silver cloudlets shone in the east above gray hills. As the light grew, the cloudlets flushed to pink, deepened to rose, then flared to scarlet. The hills grew sharp and blue, revealing peaks and ridges I could not remember having seen before.

The sun rose, filling the sky with so much of its glory that some spilled over and ran along the tops of the mountains. I watched for a moment, then because the day held no gladness without Impie, turned my back.

I was leaning over lacing my shoes, when a sound began outside the house close to the windows. It was a pattering, scratching, insistent noise. Listening intently, I told myself that some bird must be making an early promenade around the sills. Longing to look, yet fearful it might really be a bird, I finished tying my shoes.

But the unmistakable rhythm, four rapid thumps and a pause, then the same measure repeated, drew me up, and I stood staring. Running along the sill on the south was a sleek brown shape with a bushy tail. Pausing near the head of the bed, the shape looked in, and on its shoulder I saw a furrow where a claw might have raked. Then the patter, the shape and the gleaming tail disappeared, and there came the sound of shale being kicked around.

The "dollar" cookies were in a can on the floor at the foot of the bunk. With a half-dozen in my hand, I opened the door.

"Breakfast!" I yelled. "Breakfast, my lord."

His Royal Highness leaped to his perch on the bench and sat in silhouette against the shimmering glory of Mount Rainier. Eying the cookies, he rubbed his fists across his nose, scratched hastily under his arms, dropped to all fours, and came bounding toward my hand.

Shortcut: Journal Entry from a Wilderness Lookout, 28 June 1981

DON USNER

WE TOOK A LONG HIKE yesterday, to Basin Lake. Everywhere there was water, rushing right out of mountainsides and disappearing into the mossy forest floor. We arrived at the lake in late morning and walked around it until we found a place where we could get in. We intended to take baths, but a cold breeze came up and we waited. The lake sits in a granite basin about four or five miles from the lookout. The water is clear as glass.

We ate tuna and avocado—so exotic in this isolated place—and then fell asleep in the sun as the day warmed. When we woke it was still cool, but we waded into the lake and wet our heads and washed our hair on the shore, away from the water. The water made my head ache, it was so cold. But it was worth it to be clean. I took a fast plunge and shivered on the shore.

Then I got the idea to take a different route back to the lookout. I finally prevailed on Alisa and Cloud (our dog), convincing them that it would be only slightly more difficult than the trail. (How many times have I done this? It must be the "male shortcut syndrome.")

So we turned and climbed straight up the ridge behind us, to the south. After about five hundred feet, we were doing some serious rock climbing, passing Cloud up by the scruff of her neck as we made each pitch. We had some very precarious moments there, with rocks coming loose and falling down into the depths below us where the lake glittered. As we gained elevation, the immensity of the land became more and more apparent. It was much bigger than I had imagined from the safety of our little lookout.

We reached another lake basin. Snowfields from the peak that towered above reached all the way down to the water. We crossed this basin and climbed the ridge behind it—the last climb we'd have to do, I thought.

But when we topped this ridge we saw that another huge drainage separated us from the ridge that led to Butts Point—a very deep and snow-filled drainage whose opposite side was sheer and timbered thickly. Things began to look grim. But we trudged on. What else could we do? The drainage proved snowy and very cold, its streams still frozen. We had to cross huge snowfields strewn with avalanche-severed trees. "But at least we have plenty of water to drink," I said. A pathetic attempt at cheerfulness.

Then we came to the climb up out of the drainage. THE CLIMB. A horrendous scramble straight up loose slopes, short, vertical cliffs, and thick timber. We were pretty tired by the time we reached the top, where I thought we'd have it made. But from up there it was clear we had a very, very long way to go down before we would get to Butts Point. We couldn't see the lookout, but imagined it there at the end of the giant ridge before us. It seemed a very tiny outpost in this vast and wild land.

Our feet were soaking wet and a cold wind began howling. We ate our last apple and a handful of cherries. This long ridge—Butts Ridge, I'll call it, since it leads out to Butts Point—was a miserable place to walk. Through drift after drift I led on, breaking trail. We became exhausted from wallowing in deep, wet snow and climbed to high, rocky spine to find less snow. Far below to the north we could see the clearing of the abandoned Butts Point airstrip. We headed for it as a landmark. But along the way in the woods I strayed off course, and we found ourselves wading through boggy, wet thickets as the sun began to set. Finally, we came to the trail and trudged the final mile to reach the tower at dusk.

We ate oatmeal for dinner, then slept. A hard day, but rewarding after all. I learned that the ridges and peaks that look so near and friendly and easy to traverse are actually an immense and rugged landscape that can swallow a person as sure as the ocean. I am humbled.

Editor's note: Butts Creek Point lookout is no longer staffed except for emergencies. It is located above the Salmon River Canyon in the heart of Idaho's Frank Church Wilderness. There is no road access.

The Big Ugly:
Notes from a Fire Lookout

Jackie Johnson Maughan

WELL, IT'S WEDNESDAY, August 19, which means thirty-eight days
since I came up this mountain . . . address: NE of the SW, Section 33,
Township 33 North, Range 8 East, Coolwater Ridge, Selway District,
Nez Perce National Forest.

It's been two weeks of hot, dry weather—Red Flag warnings for
high winds and dry lightning, Lightning Activity Level 6 on a scale of
6. But Shissler and Gardiner lookouts over on the Selway-Bitterroot
Wilderness have had all the fire action. All I've had are two smokes, and
one was a test set by my boss since I'm a rookie.

Dispatch gives the weather every morning at 0900. This is a major
event. I turn the radio up loud, pencil poised. The good ones read it
nice and slow. Today's factors are not high for lightning or fires: widely
scattered thundershowers, winds 4–12, Lightning Activity Level 2–3, a
cooling trend predicted.

The day unwinds at its usual pace: little gold birds (finches, war-
bling vireos?) picking ladybugs off the rain gauge; kestrel on top of flag-
pole; lunch of pancakes and peanut butter. (I've run out of bread.)
I alternate between trying to write and getting up to pace the catwalk
and scan for smokes.

My boss was last up here a month ago. She left me with summer
squash and lettuce and cantaloupe and a list of things to do: paint the
inside of the lookout (including the ceiling), caulk the windows, sand
and varnish the fire-finder cabinet, fix the railings down at the spring,
dig rocks out of the road (fat chance). I have fixed the railings and

caulked the windows and begun on the cabinet. I'll have to stop with my writing soon and get to work on painting.

So what do I do all day? Air the sheets, make the bed, heat water to do dishes, clean out the stove and take the ashes down to the privy to keep down the smell, wash the floor with the gray water from doing the dishes, conduct fly-killing forays twice daily, which also means cleaning the windows (nineteen of them) twice daily, watch birds, watch the pikas, put up the flag and take it down, try to figure out animal tracks, split wood, haul water, talk to the visitors who make it up this terrible road. (I've had to leave my own car down at the ranger station because it won't clear the rocks.)

The closest lookouts I can see are Indian Hill and Pilot Knob at twenty miles. The farthest is Sheep Hill at forty miles. She's perched on top of a bald, twin-peaked mountain. If I didn't know it was a lookout, I'd swear it was a rock outcropping. Can't see Shissler, Gardiner, Salmon Mountain, Chair Point, Carey Dome, or Oregon Butte because of mountains. But I can hear them on the radio.

Storms usually take shape off to the southwest. They form here in the early afternoon as air from Oregon's high desert pushes up against the mountains of western Idaho. One seems to be collecting down there right now, but it doesn't look like much.

An hour passes. Two hours. I can hear faint thunder in the distance. No visitors so far. My cousin and his wife used to work the Huckleberry Mountain lookout up on the Panhandle Forest. He told me that when they saw visitors coming, they'd lock up the lookout and go hide in the rocks.

The usual radio traffic: fisheries crew looking for each other, trail contractor looking for partner, lost mules, lost keys, logger missing his permit, air patrol doing smoke reconnaissance.

1700. The lookouts on the southern part of the forest do their afternoon check-ins an hour later than we do. Sheep Hill comes on with her lilting voice: "Looks like this cell's turning into a big ugly. The bottom's black and the top's at maybe thirty-five thousand." I take the binoculars and look. All I can see is a bunch of gray stuff.

When I go out to jog at 1730, the air feels damp and heavy. Mountain bluebirds rush from tree to tree in small droves. Farther down, a rough-legged hawk calls and calls. I try to watch it but must keep my eyes on this road.

An hour later and I'm back at the lookout. I climb the stairs, cold already. The wind has picked up and dries the sweat and dirt to my skin. I unlock the chain and push up the trapdoor. Up on the catwalk, raindrops splat against the wood.

I go inside and sit on the bed and pull off my shoes and socks. The storm is moving now, maybe fifteen miles an hour. The gray stuff has collected into a genuine thunderhead. I can make out the anvil shape and the towering column—exactly what I've been worrying about all summer. And behind it come the fire reports: Oregon Butte, Salmon Mountain.

It moves my way slowly. Fire reports now from Carey Dome and Chair Point. The easterly lookouts aren't getting hit because the storm is tracking north. Maybe it will track right by me and up into the Panhandle.

I go out on the catwalk to see what I can see and notice an odd noise, then realize it's the antennas humming with ambient electricity. I get back inside in a hurry. The absolute worst place to be is on the catwalk. Inside, you're protected by the grounding system. Still, one's instinct when a storm is brewing is not to remain on top of the highest mountain. I have to fight with myself not to hike on down to the trees.

Inside again and the radio's going bonkers: calls for smoke jumpers, airtankers, helicopters with buckets, fire engines, and ground crews for perhaps a dozen fires. There's not much to do but listen. I can only piece together what's happening. Often all I hear is one end of the transmission. Can't hear the field crews unless they're in line with my antennas.

It's 2000 now and the storm has moved up the corridor. It's a mean-looking beast, coming in at eye level, flat black bottom sinking fangs of vertical lightning into the earth. It comes in over the Camas Prairie and hovers over Corral Hill. Then *boom, boom, boom,* it puts down three huge strikes. Then more and more, all in the same place. A half hour later, I hear the engine crew on the radio. They're on scene and have a pretty good brush fire.

Fifteen minutes later, Pilot Knob is really getting hammered. *Boom!* A huge strike, *boom, boom, boom.* Then there's a sixty-foot pillar of fire just below the lookout where he can't see it. Indian Hill calls me. Switch to channel 2. Can I see that fire?

I give him my azimuth and he calls in the cross reading.

2100. It's over me now. It's completely black outside and down come the strikes, enormous bursts of light that seem to rip open the sky, the light so bright it hurts my eyes. I've turned the radio off (out of service for lightning) and am now sitting on the bed. At first I hide under the covers but decide that's stupid. The bed is fairly safe because the frame is made of wood, unlike those in the old lookouts, with their metal cots and springs. During storms, lookouts used to stand on little wooden stools. I've got one here, about a foot high with little glass cups that screw onto its legs. I use it for a nightstand. God, to think of a night like this perched on that little stool with only glass insulator cups between me and 1.5 million volts of electricity.

Ten, perhaps fifteen, minutes later, a lull in the storm. I find my flashlight, turn on the radio, go to the fire finder, and start working up legal locations of the fires. You're not supposed to get between the fire finder and any of the metal fixtures (wood stove, propane oven, refrigerator) because they're grounded and lightning could arc and you'll get fried. This is hard to do, since the fire finder is exactly in the middle of the lookout. I move fast and have to guess where the fires are, since it's hard to see through the peephole to the crosshairs in the dark and it's hard to see the map and I can't see the lay of the land at all except when a lightning strike lights it up.

I compare sightings with Indian Hill. Our boss is also on the radio. We're talking back and forth, giving her our azimuths so she can do a transect, estimating the size of the fires. Then the antennas start to hum and the radio starts to crackle or *click, click, click* with electricity, and the storm starts putting down more lightning. I reach to shut the radio off and it shocks me, and I dive for the bed.

Again the sky lights up. And the thunder comes. And my fourteen-by-fourteen-foot room shakes and shakes, and I wonder if the shutters will come crashing down and send glass flying. Fifteen minutes pass. I've got fires on a 280. Then we're back on the radio. Our boss wants jumpers ordered at first light . . . there are so many fires forestwide that jumpers and everything else are in short supply.

August 21. Two days later and the weather's turned cold and wet, but not wet enough to put out the fires. We've got three big ones, one directly across the river canyon from me. It lies like a butterfly across the ridge and into two drainages, beautiful to see at night, but I feel bad for the fire fighters working in the cold and wet and dark. And the ridge is steep, probably seventy-five degrees. I'd like to go down on the fire line and help. I'm not really needed much, so I jump at the chance to relay when something or other breaks down and base can't hear them.

1922. There comes a priority emergency from Chair Point. "All stations clear channel." This means the entire forest. There is absolute silence. Priority emergency means life-and-death. The radio is silent for an entire hour. No explanation. Somebody somewhere's in trouble. Is it my boss's crew? That cute cowgirl redhead, that strong serious fellow, that rock and roller with the gold earring?

2107. Priority emergency's been lifted, and the person in charge on my fire radios that they're pulling out to a safety area because of high winds and flaming canopy. He requests a strike team, helicopter with bucket, tanker with retardant, sawyers (two teams), breakfasts, and radio batteries. I don't think the Forest Service could operate without radio batteries.

Five days later, it's warmed up and I hike the fifty-four-hundred-foot, six-mile drop down to the river. I can hear helicopters going *whop, whop, whop.* Then I'm out of the trees and down to the road. I'm amazed at what I see. The fires are under control or mostly out, and the crews are mopping up. O'Hara Flats looks like a military command center. A tent city of four hundred people, generators chugging, miles of electrical cord and cable, water trucks, hot shower trucks, food trucks, gear trucks, dozens of blue Porta-potties, communications tent, medical tents, mess tents, crew tents, private tents, school buses, vans, jeeps, pickups.

It's not hard to hitch a ride to the ranger station to pick up my mail. It's quiet here with the sprinklers going on the big front lawn. I get a Pepsi from the machine and step out back. There in the afternoon sun, packing long, long lengths of fire hose, is Ruth, my cowgirl friend. The yellow jackets hover about as we talk. It turns out she was on that crew the priority emergency was called on. They were almost trapped in a grass fire. I never do get the story straight, but apparently two crews were involved, cut off from one another.

She keeps talking while she works—something about rolling rocks and going into the black.

I take off my daypack, wave away the wasps, and sit down. Rolling rocks? Rolling rocks, she repeats, a catch in her voice. It was nighttime and the canyon was steep, and a fire can burn away the undergrowth holding rocks in place. Once they start to roll downhill, it's really scary because you can't see them. You can hear them when they come rumbling down, but you have to guess where they're going to land. Guess wrong and you're pressed duck.

I think about that for a while. It's pretty easy to visualize, especially the part about pressed duck. But what, I ask her, does she mean about going into the black?

She stops her work while she talks. Going into the black means you go into an area that's already burned.

I have some trouble with this part. I ask her to explain.

The best place to go when a fire looks like it might catch you is into an area that's already burned over because there's not as much fuel there.

I understand this well enough but realize that the only way I could figure out exactly what happened with the two crews and all is if she drew a map.

Well, she's almost got one canvas backpack filled with fire hose. It's nice the way she lays it down in flat ribbons. I don't ask her any more about going into the black because I don't want her to think I'm slow.

I uncross my legs and recross them, noticing they're pretty dirty. I study a yellow jacket as it lands on my Pepsi can. Already I'm starting to worry about getting organized and back up the mountain. Yes, it really was a big ugly.

Rattlesnake Tales

Nomeca Hartwell

EVERY SUMMER I HOPE it won't happen. But I know in my heart of hearts that this is wishful thinking. Still, I greet the summer warmth on Sexton Mountain with a sense of joy and peacefulness. Until that moment arrives.

No more walking in the tall grasses. No more clambering over rocks or going barefoot on the lawn at night. I allow only so many days of grace for Mr. Rattlesnake to move on. After that, he's a dead snake.

It's been this way since anyone can remember. Back in 1916, the very first fire lookouts on Sexton worried about keeping rattlesnakes out of their tent-on-a-platform. Thirty years later, my station correspondence indicates that harassed personnel were requesting a fence to keep the rattlesnakes out of the area.

I suppose I'm lucky. I don't live in a tent. I don't have to deal with the rattlesnakes that used to live under the sidewalk. I don't have to hike past the snake pits that once existed along the two-mile trail that leads to the top of the mountain. (One story from the forties holds that a new employee was on her way up to the work site on top of the mountain when she came across a rattlesnake. About face and back down the hill she went, never to be seen again.)

Still, I hate to take the life of anything.

I can't remember which was the first rattler I had to kill up here, but I surely do remember the various locations they have occupied. One of the strangest was behind the house (the Weather Service station that I operate year-round). I walked into the backyard and glanced in the direction of our oversize rabbit cage that hugged the back wall of the house. There in the chicken-wire hutch, which was six inches off the ground, was a nice, fat rattlesnake stretched out leisurely sipping at the rabbits' water bottle.

It's not the snakes themselves that stir up the adrenaline; it's the fact that the ground has become a minefield of possibilities. A friend who was carrying a bowl of water outside for the dog nearly stepped on a large rattler when she reopened the side door. Her voice on the phone an hour later told me that she was still revved up. That snake measured forty plus inches.

I had a similar experience in the garage one summer. I went into the huge metal-and-concrete building, got what I needed, and was about to exit. There by the door, curled up inside on the cool floor, was a rattler. I hollered to the relief lookout to come to my aid, and we finished off the poor thing with shovels. What really bothered me later on was the fact that he must have been there all along. Possibly I'd even stepped over him.

Trust me, I have had my go-rounds with other creatures that inhabit this venerable mountain. There were three porkies I herded into a garbage can one night to save my garden. I carried them off to the next township. And sixteen tomato-chomping chipmunks that I trapped in a cage and eventually deposited at a rest stop along the freeway. And how can I forget the mouse population that got into my car's air-conditioning system not once, but twice? When I came home one night, turned down the bedcovers, and found mouse poop in my sheets, that did it. Forget about preserving the songbird population, I got a cat. One cat led to another, and now I have three killers on the job full-time. I've probably been in more danger from would-be snake killers, one in particular, than I ever have from the rattlers themselves.

Karen, my relief lookout, had a black lab named Raven. Raven's face had swelled up to double its normal size one Labor Day weekend. We assumed it was a wasp sting and treated it accordingly, only to find out later that the dog had been bitten by a rattler and the preferred treatment was just the opposite of what we'd done.

Karen and I shared work duties for several summers, and I enjoyed her company. But she'd never used a rifle, a pistol, or a shotgun. When a rattler showed up under the bottom steps of the lookout, she danced around those stairs in her white socks (no shoes), aiming her dad's rifle at flowers, bushes, the fence, the sky, rocks, pebbles. She tried and tried, but just couldn't do this snake in.

Finally, I asked if I should take over. I took aim, was ready, but the damn gun wouldn't fire. So I ended up getting a Colt 32 from my place and hit the bull's-eye, so to speak, which impressed both me and Karen at the time. Later I found out that the only thing wrong with her dad's rifle was that she'd had the safety on when she thought it was off and vice versa. Then I remembered with something close to horror how she'd waved that thing around thinking the safety was on.

The snake stories never seem to end. In fact, they are the one constant on this prominent mountain overlooking the Grants Pass area. The Indian Wars of the 1850s have long since ceased (the road north to Mount Sexton runs red with blood), and the days of the Sacramento-Portland stagecoach robberies in Sexton Gulch are long gone. Even the Pacific Highway over the Pass, completed in the first years of the lookout, has been obliterated by the I-15 freeway.

But just yesterday I was up in the lookout and heard a strange buzzing sound. I said to myself, "That *can't* be what I think I'm hearing, not way up here—could it?" I stepped outside onto the porch overlooking the hillside, and down below I saw my once-bit tomcat eagerly teasing and pawing at something on the concrete slab half buried in the bushes. Summer had arrived again.

Night Call

SUE CURTISS

THE FIR TREES are dull green in the moonlight, their shadows flat, black, against the white rocks. The lake is a huge, silver mirror. Somewhere below, an owl hoots, maybe hoping to startle an unwary mouse into movement.

Sometimes, when the wind blows just right though the metal fretwork, my tower sings. I listen to it now—just a small, three-note thread of sound that mingles with the other night sounds below.

The phone rings. I pick it up, irritated that someone would call this late.

He whispers, "All alone up there?"

"Who is this?" I ask.

"You don't know me," he says. "But I know you. Aren't you afraid up there, all by yourself? Anything could happen . . ."

I flip on the tower lights, and he laughs. "Turned the lights on, huh? Scared of the dark?"

I listen, frozen, as he whispers on and on, then, finally, manage to hang up.

My hands are shaking; I try to light a cigarette and can't. My cat, wakened by the phone and lights, rubs against my ankles; as I scoop him up, burying my face and hands in the soft, warm fur, the phone rings again. I listen to the ringing, with the cat purring in my arms, for a long, long time.

When it stops I take the phone off the hook. A sudden movement startles me; someone is standing behind me, and I'm clear across the tower before I realize it's my own reflection in a window.

Now I see my reflection in all the windows—a distorted, strange image.

I check to make sure the trapdoor is down and locked, then put the phone back on the hook, lock my door, and turn out the lights.

The wind is stronger; the tower is still singing, but now it's a moan that raises the hair on my arms and makes the dark threatening.

A coyote calls in the distance; I wait, watching the silver lake and the flat, black shadows under the trees, until the tiny three-note thread of song returns and blends again into the familiar hilltop sounds.

"Everything's back to normal," I think. "There's no one here but me. I'm alone."

Then the phone rings, and rings and rings.

The Omelet

BART EBEN

THE YEAR OF 1992 was a good one for mushrooms in Bear Valley, but because of drought, the season didn't last very long. I did manage to pick enough to make quite a few good meals before the season ended, and on several backpacking trips I almost lived off them.

In the evenings I would usually take my family—Smokey, a 145-pound three-fourths wolf–one-fourth malamute; Wizard, a miniature poodle; and Gypsy, a 100 percent, full-blooded biting boss bitch—on a hike until dark.

On one of these outings I came across a large cluster of beautiful wild mushrooms. They seemed to have been grazed upon by deer, so I reasoned they must be okay: I didn't see any sick or dead deer lying around, and I reasoned that surely deer were smart enough to know what to eat and what not to. And they certainly looked good enough to me, so I gave them the old "If they don't bite your tongue, they're safe" test. They passed. In fact, they were quite tasty. When I uprooted them, an underground root runner came up with them. With an armload of these delicacies, I happily headed back to the lookout, gloating over my booty.

I have a buddy, Howard, over on the Jackson Peak lookout whose idea of gourmet eating is tacos; in fact, I think it's the only thing he knows how to cook. But usually he lives on spaghetti and chicken soup. (I'm not sure he even takes it out of the can.)

So when I got back, I just couldn't help myself. I had to call him. "Howard," I bragged, "guess what I'm having for breakfast?" Howard sort of grunted, and I took this to mean that he was just burning up with curiosity.

And so I described my wild mushroom omelet complete with ham and sharp cheddar cheese and maybe some finely chopped onion.

His long, thoughtful answer was, "Well, I hope you vomit it all up."

The next morning as I prepared my beauties, I noticed that the root section seemed to be just like the stems, so into the omelet it went. The omelet was delicious, and I felt quite satisfied with my meal, especially knowing that Howard was probably heating up leftover tacos for breakfast.

As I prepared to wash the morning dishes, I noticed that the dishpan was moving in a strange circular pattern. I looked away and then back again, and sure enough, it was really moving. I felt perfectly fine, though things were beginning to look "different." I decided to sit down on the bed for a while. But then the room began to spin, lights began to flash, and up came the omelet. I felt a little better and thought I'd rest a few minutes. I lay down, and the next thing I knew, I was waking up and *brother!* now I really felt weird. My vision was like one of those old movie projectors when a frame would stick. It seemed as though I could see out of the back of my head: Things that I knew were behind me were now flashing in front of me, lights and all! It was a very spooky feeling.

I stumbled over to the radio and called Boise Dispatch.

"Russ," I said, "I think I might be in trouble." Then I tried to describe what was happening to me and I think I may have mentioned the mushrooms.

"You're going to be all right, Bart," Russ said. "I have help on the way. Just keep talking to me."

The next thing I knew, I was lying on my bed staring up at the faces of a whole lookout full of fire fighters.

"What the hell are you guys doing here?" I asked in my confusion. They had heard my conversation with Dispatch and made a helicopter trip across Bear Valley to my mountain.

One of the fire fighters, Mick, who is an emergency medical technician, was trying to get me settled down so he could put an oxygen mask on my face. All the while he kept saying, "You're going to be all right. Life Flight is on its way."

I looked out the window, and helicopter 30 Bravo was sitting just below the lookout with its rotor turning.

"Why don't you take me in that one? I'm strong. I'll show you." I slid to the foot of the bed, put my feet on the floor, and stood up.

I looked down and *wow!*, my legs looked like they were three stories long!

But then my mind fixed on 30 Bravo again. "Take me in this one," I argued, and stormed for the door. Then I was out the door and down the path, headed for the helicopter.

At this point I must have lost consciousness. I was told later that it took several fire fighters to wrestle me down before I could reach the rotating blades of the helicopter.

The next thing I remember is being en route to Boise and looking down at the forest I love so much. Then we were out of the forest and landing on the roof of the hospital, and there, waiting for me, was my eldest daughter.

"What the hell are you doing here?" I asked.

"What the hell are *you* doing here?" she demanded.

"Well, I guess I must have eaten some of those funny mushrooms, and they took me on a trip," I confessed.

"Some trip," she scolded. "What are you doing eating things that you aren't sure are safe?"

From there on it seemed like everyone wanted to test my patience. All I wanted was a bed. But they held me hostage for what seemed like forever. I protested loudly, but I was outnumbered. I don't remember what all the tests were that they performed; all I remember is wanting to sleep.

The next morning I was in no mood to stay in this place any longer. I looked in the closet and there hung my clothes, and in a heartbeat I was dressed and headed out the door.

"Where are you going?" the nurse demanded.

"Out of here!"

"The doctor hasn't released you yet. He wants you to stay another day. Get back in bed."

"Forget it. I'm out of here," I said.

"Well, I'll have to get a wheelchair. It's hospital policy."

"Forget it. I'll meet you at the front desk."

When I got to the lobby, who do you suppose was there to greet me? Howard! And Beth, my boss.

We hugged and shook hands, and Howard apologized for his wish that I vomit up my beautiful omelet.

After a lengthy scolding, my daughter made me promise never

again to eat wild mushrooms until I learned which ones are safe. She bought me a book about them.

That same afternoon, she drove me back to my beloved place in the forest, Whitehawk lookout.

After a little research, it was determined that the mushrooms in Eben's omelet were probably psilocybin.

Going Away

Miles Wilson

As we begin our account it is June and Mr. Parker has come to Blueridge to salvage the accumulation of his life. The debris, as he puts it, of forty years. To accomplish this he carries a typewriter, four thousand dollars in traveler's checks, and his Navy trunk, dredged from the garage and packed sparingly. Travel light, travel far, Mr. Parker invents and the phrase lodges with him, inserting itself like a souvenir in conversations with himself.

Behind, Mr. Parker has left a divorce, a resignation. Husband, father, personnel systems response analyst, he has a citation for putting together a management package for the particleboard industry in China. And now he has come to Blueridge to assemble his life. Not *re*assemble, he insists in a draft of his first memo, for clearly it has never been intact. An easy judgment perhaps; common enough, certainly. In making it, Mr. Parker reveals to us much of his circumstance: drifting into his forties, he had come first to fear and then to believe that things which once mattered made no sense anymore, that the life he had arranged for himself was a pale fabrication, that he must achieve substance now or go to the grave a figment. He is not sure how true this is, but it seems true enough to act on. He leaves without telling anyone where he is going, without knowing himself. He chooses only not to leave the state. In some oblique way, that forestalls the sense of running away.

His wife was Barbara; his children, Stephanie, Scott, and Shannon. As an undergraduate, he once wrote half of what he explained was a Jamesian novel about growing up. For fifteen years, he has written only checks and memos. His wife writes all letters, even those to his parents. Now, with everything at stake, he begins again to write. He decides to

call this material "memos." It is one of the few ironies he permits himself. For our purposes it is not necessary to know more. Except, perhaps, that he has just reread *Heart of Darkness*. This should afford us
some perspective, some charity, in considering the psychological excess
of his first memo.[1]

We may pass over this and future memos with little comment. They
do, however, reveal of Mr. Parker a certain florid fluency which is less
apparent in his conduct. This disparity narrows later, for we shall see
language come to fail Mr. Parker as it becomes a more responsive image
of its source.

He occupies the first afternoon in Blueridge writing and revising
the memo. Finished, he is proud of its unsparing condemnations, its
apocalyptic resolve. Later, when he reads it to the girl he will live with,
she shrugs and says, "To thine own self . . ." It has always sounded like
good advice to Mr. Parker. The girl adds, "And all that shit."

After supper Mr. Parker ponders between beginning some of Mal-
colm Lowry's late, long, redemptive stories and investigating the local
tavern. Isolation, he decides, will more likely make him a surly recluse
than a saint.

The Firs is much like any beer bar in a small town in western Oregon. It contains a counter, stools, some cramped booths, a country-
western jukebox, a shuffleboard and pool table, walls littered with signs

---

[1] I am forty-three years old. And I have learned that betrayal cores the heart
of man. I would not claim this a contribution to human knowledge for we know
it, all of us. But we remember, are called to acknowledge this, only as a collective
accretion. Mass insanities of race, nation, or ideology—collective betrayal is plain,
monstrous, and incalculable. It is this which enables us to assume some unspecifi-
able part as our responsibility and be done with it. For the ocean of such betrayal
cannot be fathomed, and that which is not fathomable is not truly our own.

This much is clear. But it is not such betrayals which concern me here.
Rather, it is a singular betrayal which I, full of misshapen notions of responsibility,
created, nourished, sinewed into acts, and now must claim as my own. When I
confess I am soul-sickened by the enormity of what I have done, I must insist that
I speak as one who is rigorously descriptive. To judge this betrayal would be the
most pedestrian exercise in irrelevance and worse. For judgment presumes to balance books, right scales, bring act and consequence into adjustment. It is the
lackey of conscience, the refuge of those who feed their souls on the exceedingly
fine grindings of the mills of morality.

No, judgment will not do. For I have relinquished my life. Faithful to the
corrosive imperatives of the world, sucking the canker of comfort, I have sanitized
those imperatives I suspected in myself. And I have come here, now, to resurrect
those imperatives, redeem those betrayals, to find, if I dare, my own substance.
The alternative to success in this is unthinkable.

and artifacts, linoleum floors, and smelly restrooms. A sign above the cash register reads "In God We Trust—All Others Pay Cash." The tavern is run by a genial owner and a divorced barmaid with two children. We detail it here because the Firs will become a landmark in Mr. Parker's new geography.

Mr. Parker, a gin-and-tonic man, remembers, coming through the door, how good beer used to be in college. He gets drunk and has a good time—losing at pool, losing at shuffleboard, winning the music at dice, throwing up when he gets back to his room. Travel light, travel far, he gurgles consolingly, hanging over the toilet.

In the morning Mr. Parker drives to the coast, gets sunburned, eats raw oysters, drives back at night with the windows open, sleeps till noon. When Mrs. Honnold asks how long he'll be staying, he gives her a month's rent.

Mr. Parker becomes a regular at the Firs. A bottle of Budweiser arrives without asking when he comes in. To nourish the beer-sloshed rapport with his new companions, he drives again to the coast, to Newport for a few days, learning to drink beer and shoot pool at some anonymous tavern. When he returns, he still loses, but not as badly.

His second memo follows the first by several weeks and is more temperate—though it deteriorates through several revisions. Its excesses are those we might expect in a man trying on new metaphors to accommodate beginnings.[2]

Mr. Parker is encouraged by the speed and clarity of this recognition, but he has read enough to know that the motions of the heart are deceptive, to suspect the easy, the obvious. He would like to discover how they chose among possible selves, or whether they had to. Mr. Parker is not sure how to approach such questions. Instead, he asks about fishing and local history.

Although the blueprint of Mr. Parker's new architecture does not allow for it, he becomes aware of three women. Marge, the barmaid, is

---

[2] It is imperative that a man be among men, and though lacking the substance that anchors and animates, I have found men to be among. They lack complex intelligence, clearly they are not entirely happy, yet I find them unmistakably human and that, first and finally, is what matters. They are human because they possess themselves. They do not relinquish the world, but the self is not derivative, it comes abundantly from inside. It is theirs. And it is right. And it is a large measure of what I seek. They have such limiting options, yet they have pursued selves as unique as fingerprints, true as carbon steel into old fir. I value them for this, and while I do not wish to imitate their forms, the true, tough fiber of their lives is the strength and substance which I seek.

quick, bitter, and can land on her feet from any posture. May, an awesome drinker, is older and through three husbands. She contains a voluptuous pace, attractive to uncertain men. And Adrian. Almost a graduate of Mills College, she had lived in the Spanish Sahara for two years in hazy circumstances, had undertaken abortions in Mexico City, Gibraltar, and Oakland, and had come, amazingly, to Blueridge, for reasons similar to Mr. Parker's. She supports herself on the salary from a CETA job in which she is assembling an oral history of eastern Lane County.

Mr. Parker, sensing a new and vibrant sequence, participates with enthusiasm. Adrian is often lethargic, which encourages him to frisk outside his old protective reserve with women. In two weeks of beer and mutual confidings, both have talked out their histories. After such confidings there is nothing to do but live together.

They rent a small house west of town. The loggers, who have been unsuccessful with Adrian and have failed to penetrate the eager friendliness of Mr. Parker for an excuse to maul him, accept the situation much as they accept the fact that the Forest Service, like rain down the backs of their necks, will be with them always. Their wives say occasionally vicious things about them at the laundromat, but they don't matter greatly, their role as moral arbiters lost back in the sixties.

After a month with Adrian, Mr. Parker is uneasy. His circumstances have altered substantially, but patterns remain unchanged. He continues to brush his teeth twice a day, he follows the baseball standings with interest, and he thinks about his past as much as ever. He drinks more now, but this was not really the sort of breakthrough he had in mind. His old self hunkers down, as if resolved to squat just out of reach until he resumes it. Perplexed, he reviews the memos to seek out how this has happened and what he might do differently. The memos, he decides, are ponderously pretentious, swollen by his inflated sense of self-magnitude in trying to remake his life. He resolves to write no more. Adrian goes to work haphazardly and is finally fired.

Through the summer they raise a garden, go fishing, smoke the marijuana that Adrian has and buy no more. Mr. Parker is glad. The smoke scours his throat, the effects are unnoticeable, and besides it's more or less illegal. Adrian moves on to herbal teas and tequila. His college alumni magazine finds him and he studies the class notes. He recognizes only a few of the names. Everyone is a success. Although he has never run before, Mr. Parker begins jogging. He quits after a week, unable to elude or pacify the town's dogs. They make love, of course, too. Mr. Parker devotes considerable energy to being mature and inventive. Adrian responds as conventionally as his wife.

They go to the ocean often. Watching the long swells come in, Adrian glazes over. At such times Mr. Parker wonders if she imagines herself a character in some foreign movie. Adrian will not admit it. Once, on the beach, Mr. Parker is sure he sees Shannon among a group of Girl Scouts. He maneuvers Adrian up toward the high tide line, rummaging through driftwood until the girls have passed.

Adrian does not speak of her family, but once some friends come through from California. They have three large dogs: Earth, Kilo, and Hoist. One is an Afghan, the other two are indecipherable. Mr. Parker cannot remember the friends' names. They sleep out front in a Volkswagen bus with West Virginia plates and eat ravenously. Mr. Parker is polite, the friends are polite. They have nothing to say to each other. After a week they leave for British Columbia.

By September Mr. Parker is going to the bar, nightly, alone. His companions there have become predictable, their selfhood nothing more than the drudge of routine. He feels cheated, but is not sure how or by whom. Whenever possible he drinks by himself. Adrian reads Joyce Carol Oates, writes letters, goes to bed early. Mr. Parker has never read Joyce Carol Oates. He finds her at first disturbing, then repetitive. He does not say so. When the rains start in November, Mr. Parker, depressed, is ready. They confirm his developing belief that life moves in dismal cycles, tending always toward winter.

In December, three days before his anniversary, Mr. Parker explains he has business with his bank. The lie animates him for several days, but Adrian doesn't notice. He drives to Portland, parks in a downtown garage, rents another car, and drives past his home three times. The Buick is in the driveway, along with a car he doesn't recognize. The house has been painted a different color. When he calls later from a bar, ready to disguise his voice, not knowing what he will say, no one is home.

Adrian is asleep when he returns. After he has persistently touched her awake, she says it is her period and asks him to rub her back.

She leaves in December, a week before Christmas. Mr. Parker returns from the bar one afternoon and she is gone. He is stricken with an urgent sense of relief. Travel light, travel far, he repeats giddily, dusting shelves, changing sheets, cleaning the bathroom.

He goes home that night with Marge, marveling at such quick luck. He wakes once at the sound of a pickup, certain one of the loggers will come through the door and hit him in the stomach before he can get his pants on. In the morning he rises before the others and fixes breakfast. The two children pour sugar on the table, spill milk, and the boy tells Marge to fuck herself when she slaps him for neglecting his burned eggs.

Mr. Parker goes home, sleeps, goes out, buys a bottle, comes home, and writes the last memo we shall consider here.[3] If we detect an aroma of desperation, it is because Mr. Parker is getting scared.

The winter is tenacious. Mr. Parker invents a letter. The rain, he will write, grows moss on his soul. He suffers the bucolic plague. If death consumes us all, what's left but life? He cannot think of anyone to send the letter to.

By March Mr. Parker has three hundred dollars and the rent is due. Although he lives frugally, eating little, the beer and a quart of gin, drunk straight, every three and a half days, have depleted him. Adrian has depleted him. There is no call here for personnel systems response analysts, but leaving Blueridge for such a place has never been admissible.

The rain stops early. Mr. Parker buys jeans, boots, gloves, suspenders, and tries three logging companies. He had set chokers one summer during college. But the woods are tight, real loggers are out of work. Mr. Parker thinks this is bad luck for him. It is not.

The other employer in Blueridge is the Forest Service. Mr. Parker takes a Civil Service exam and watches his money recede. His score, finally, is the second highest ever recorded on the Blueridge Ranger District. Sized up as too old for strenuous fieldwork, he is offered a job as a lookout. In early June the Forest Service packer hauls him in to Walker Mountain.

Straddling a divide between the McKenzie and Willamette drainages, commanding a view of rich timber country and a large chunk of wilderness to the east, Walker Mountain is one of the few manned lookouts remaining in the Cascades. It can be reached by trail and by Forest Service radio. At that elevation, in that solitude, the radio sounds like the voice of God.

Ninety feet up in the tower, storing supplies, Mr. Parker discovers a note left by his immediate, perhaps his only, predecessor. The packer

---

[3] I   I must act to change my understanding.
II I must try to understand my acts.
III I must convert my acts to change.
IV Trying to convert my understanding, I must change my act.

has said that Frank was on the mountain every summer for thirty-seven years. The note, printed carefully across the top of a fire sighting form, is written in fierce red ink: "The roof leaks over the stove."

After a week Mr. Parker has called in two controlled slash burns, smoke from the Pope & Talbot mill, a campfire at the Stony Meadow Recreation Site, and a pocket of fog on upper Piecemeal Creek. He can't understand much of what goes on over the radio and he no longer wears clothes. Travel light, travel far, he says, cleaning the tower's windows with his underwear.

Once a month the packer brings food, a paycheck, company. The packer drinks hugely and will talk all night about fires.

Mr. Parker begins to experiment. Dry needles, cones, bark, dead manzanita and fern. He keeps a record of how they ignite, burn, go out. The packer brings stubby candles and he tests them too. Once, just before dark, an owl flies into the glass. Mr. Parker, studying maps, lurches up, terrified. That night he bolts the door. In the morning the owl is gone from the walkway.

By September Mr. Parker is ready. He has begun jogging again, plodding along the trail to his lookout, and can run four miles without stopping. He also has a potato sack of cedar needles and dried manzanita leaves, twenty candles, and a well-marked map.

The burning index rises and stays high. College begins and the summer help quits, leaving the fire crews depleted. He waits for an east wind, and it comes. The forest is closed, logging shut down. The Forest Service, the Governor, everybody declares a fire emergency. On the radio the Blueridge Fire Control Officer exhorts Mr. Parker to watch relentlessly. Mr Parker promises.

That night he finds Frank's note and prints beneath it: "The floor leaks under the stove." He does not know if this is true, but it seems probable. Leaving the lookout, hiking hard, he sets candles and kindling at the base of steep east slopes, in roadless country, visible only from his lookout.

Two days later he is done, watching smoke from his second fire swell into the sky miles away. Four of his fires go, two don't. They are controlled after burning twenty thousand acres. Mr. Parker hikes out, boards a Greyhound in Crescent, heads south. Travel light, travel far, he repeats. He is no longer sure what this means, but it seems a familiar comfort. He is not surprised when the FBI arrests him at the Sacramento depot.

His divorce becomes final during the trial, where psychiatrists alternately declare him accountable and unaccountable for burning up 130,000,000 board feet of Willamette National Forest timber. Some come from Blueridge to testify, Adrian cannot be found, his family stays away. The federal prosecutor introduces the kindling notes, left at the lookout, as evidence of his intelligence, rationality, purpose. The less lucid memos seem to have vanished.

Mr. Parker, having neither explanation nor remorse, has no defense. In court, he is congenial to everyone but otherwise takes little interest in the case. After presentence investigation, he receives three years for arson. His attorney is outraged. Mr. Parker refuses to allow an appeal to be filed.

In prison he is inconspicuous and enjoys the small privileges of inmates who are not criminals. He begins what he describes as a Kafkaesque novel about growing up and after a year assumes editorship of the prison newspaper. In national competition with weekly papers published at institutions of more than five hundred but fewer than a thousand inmates, it receives third place. His own column, "Convictions," is singled out for special mention.

So we have encountered Mr. Parker, followed his horizontal progress, and now must pass on to other matters. But what are we to make of this? Surely, the seeking of a better self engages our best wishes and support. Aberrations in pursuit of that self provide a certain interest. Adrian, Blueridge, the family are admittedly pallid, but that is not our concern. And the memos, once promising, serve in the end, as does most language, the prosecuting attorneys of our world. How, then, account to the worm of consequence for time spent here?

A possibility reveals itself and I will advance it, enforce it even. We may leave our fiction, exiting through one of Mr. Parker's recent columns: "Only this: That the world is a hard place for us all, that resolve to change our lives is seldom enough, that damaged men, grounded in blundering circumstance, merit neither compassion nor lament but human affirmation as one of us—all of us. We must believe this, we must believe this I swear it, or we can believe nothing else again."

The Telescoping Effect

Jackie Johnson Maughan

THE PASSAGE OF TIME compresses memory so that certain events, certain years, stand out in topographic relief. In mountaineering it's called the telescoping effect: small features flatten, slopes appear steeper. You lose the detail but come to understand the shape.

Two years stand out in my mind, one in front of the other. In 1977 my father died. In 1980 my husband turned up missing.

My dad was an outfitter and guide in Idaho's River of No Return country. My husband was part of the cadre of environmentalists who labored through the 1970s to preserve it as wilderness. And it is this third component, the idea and fact of wilderness, that informs the other two.

My dad stood six feet, seven inches and weighed three hundred pounds. Massive as a mountain and bald as a granite dome. Though a former professional ball player, he favored poetry and, in fact, wrote it better than most.

My husband is one of those odd professors of political science who actually likes politics. He knows how to get things done and works on public land issues as though he were paid for it, and people come to him with every sort of problem from BLM grazing regulations to timber sales in critical grizzly bear habitat.

So when he turned up missing in a freak snowstorm, it occurred to me that the loss would be more than my own. It turned out that a lot of other people felt the same way, which is one of the things that makes this story easier to tell.

Late May in Idaho is not an especially pleasant time to go backpacking. But then it's not an especially dangerous time either, if you stick to the lower elevations.

And that's what Ralph had planned. A few days into the Birch Creek area. High desert mountains of caverns, arches, antelope, and trout that make your fishing pole bob like a witching wand.

Ralph is no fool. He doesn't hike alone into mountain blizzards. He reads books with titles like *The Metaphysics of Climate* and *Two Million Years of Weather*. He's written a trail guide to the Teton Wilderness, a place (not to be confused with Grand Teton National Park) where people are few and every boulder looks just like a grizzly bear's butt for precisely the reason it could be.

I don't remember that the Mount Saint Helens eruption two days earlier was even mentioned as he assembled his gear. But I do remember his refusal to set a specific itinerary. Birch Creek, he said, was a state of mind.

Maybe I didn't press as hard as I should have. I trusted him. He is the kind of man my dad had instantly liked. They'd hardly gotten to know each other before dad died. But I'm getting ahead of myself.

Ralph turned in early. I stayed up late thinking. Logically, there was little to fear. The Birch Creek valley is seventy-five hundred feet at its highest point. And this was a dry May, snowmelt on the surrounding mountains up to eighty-five hundred.

But I had this feeling. And before I went to bed, I put a big note on the bathroom mirror threatening to call out the National Guard if he wasn't home by Friday.

Although it didn't register consciously at the time, on an intuitive level I must have connected his leaving with my dad's ashes scattered in the mountains overlooking the River of No Return. That's where dad died, you see.

Well, Mount Saint Helens blew Sunday, May 18, and Ralph took off on Tuesday, the twentieth. There was a dusting of white ash on the Toyota, which gives you an idea of the size of the blast. Mount Saint Helens is four hundred miles away.

I was a little jealous that my job kept me home, but not enough to wish bad weather on him. When the weather report on Thursday night was for thunderstorms and scattered snow in the mountains, I didn't worry too much. He'd just pack up and come home.

Friday afternoon came, cold and gray.

Friday night, no Ralph. More snow predicted in the mountains.

Saturday night, again no Ralph, and the line between violating his freedom and possibly embarrassing him was crossed. If he was in trouble, twenty-four hours was too long to wait. I called the Idaho State Police and asked them to keep an eye out for his car.

Among the questions the night sergeant asked was one no doubt routine to him but startling to me: Were we having marital problems (had he left me)? I also remember the words "foul play" coming up, and that scared me. I'd been thinking more along the lines of snow-storm and broken leg.

The Birch Creek valley is seventy-five miles long and drains two long, narrow mountain ranges. The farthest you can get from a main road is fifteen miles. And that's what had me worried. If the car were stuck and he'd simply holed up to wait out the storm, why hadn't he hiked out when the weather broke?

What I didn't realize was just how much snow he had to contend with—a total of four feet by the time it was all over. While Mount Saint Helens can't absolutely be named responsible, a cloud of caltrop-shaped cinders reaching clear to the stratosphere is at least cause for speculation.

Sunday night and still no Ralph. It was close to midnight when I called the state police and the Clark County sheriff and officially reported him missing.

What I did next isn't logical, but I put some soup in a thermos and assembled a daypack and warm clothes and started north. I'd called a friend who lived up closer to Birch Creek, and we'd decided to start looking for him in the morning.

Fifty miles north, the absurdity of my actions dawned on me. How could Anne and I possibly hope to find him in 550 square miles of mostly unroaded land?

Back home, I began to put in motion a mobilization that ultimately would include not only most of our friends and family, but also the Idaho State University Outdoor Program, the ISU Military Science Department, a psychic, three county sheriffs' departments, fixed wing reconnaissance, a state legislator, the governor, and, yes, the National Guard.

By Monday afternoon I'd hired a pilot to overfly the country. Cloud cover was a major problem, and so were wind shears; he and Anne as spotter couldn't get low enough to see very much.

Monday evening I checked in with the Clark County sheriff. He'd been out all day driving up and down the canyons in the southern end of the valley. One man in a pickup. The task was impossible.

Meanwhile, Ralph would be out of food unless he was in good enough shape to catch fish. I felt I had no choice but to mount an independent search. I contacted the ISU Outdoor Program—moun-taineers experienced in winter search and rescue as well as friends.

We got together Ralph's topographic maps to the area and by process of elimination determined that he was probably in the northern end of the valley. Those were the maps that were missing.

The searchers were planning to move out early in the morning, and I called the Clark County sheriff to ask where he wanted us to set up a base camp. He refused our help. In fact, he told me this was his jurisdiction and he'd take care of it. I'm sure he pictured a bunch of hippies in tennis shoes flailing around out there in the snowdrifts and getting lost themselves.

While I understood his reasoning, I was absolutely unwilling to let any more time pass. Then came a notion: why not set up base camp just over the line and into the next county out of his jurisdiction? That's what we did.

The sky remained overcast and snow continued in the mountains, with temperatures in the thirties at night. We made dozens of calls. We needed four-wheel drives and two-way radios. This was how the Military Science Department became involved. They had the radios.

By Tuesday afternoon base camp was established and the searchers assembled. There were approximately thirty people equipped with army and private four-by-four vehicles, maps, radios, and mess tent. They'd located on Gilmore Summit, a windy rise near the main road. This spot, just north of the small town of Leadore, was chosen for radio communication. The plan was to start the sweep from the north and radio back after each canyon had been checked.

The press now had the story, and calls from more friends and even a few volunteers began to come in. Those who had four-wheel drives or backcountry experience I sent on up.

The weather had cleared enough for me to hire another plane, and the pilot searched from one end of the valley to the other. He found nothing.

The Lemhi and Fremont County sheriffs' departments joined in the search. The Fremont sheriff, it turned out, was taking advice from a psychic who'd had a vision that located Ralph twenty-eight miles south of Salmon, seven miles from the highway, and about a mile from his vehicle. He'd had the feeling that Ralph was alive but under some kind of stress such as that caused by an injury.

Although the vision produced no more information than what we'd come up with ourselves, it started me thinking about the circumstances of my father's death.

Dad had gotten wet while setting up camp. He went to bed without dinner and by nightfall was feeling pretty rugged. During the night his condition worsened—chills, nausea, and a rattling cough. Two members of the party set out in the dark for the Sheep Hill lookout, who radioed for help. By early morning, when the helicopter arrived, it was too late. Dad died of pneumonia, pulmonary edema, and congestive heart failure.

As I imagined my Ralph lying somewhere in the snow, a shin bone piercing his skin from a compound fracture, I kept thinking about my father. Had he been in civilization, he would have lived. The wilderness had taken him. Would the same happen to my husband?

By Tuesday night I was desperate to bring out helicopters. This would mean either calling out the National Guard or taking out a second mortgage on the house. I was ready to do both.

Among those who had offered help was a state legislator. She immediately agreed to call Governor Evans and ask him to intervene with the National Guard.

On Ralph's end, Thursday night had produced a tremendous thunderstorm. When at last the rain fell silent, the dim morning light revealed the cause—the tent was buried in two and a half feet of snow.

The blizzard continued all day Thursday and Friday. Visibility was ten feet. Leadore, the nearest town, was thirteen miles away—two to the mouth of the canyon and then eleven across a treeless sagebrush flat in zero visibility. Death if attempted.

Eventually the snow came almost to the roof of his car nearby. It was from the car radio that he learned that people were searching for him and speculating about his demise.

By Saturday his tent was leaking badly. He abandoned it to sleep in the back of his car. The weather was slowly improving, but storms continued to roll in every three to four hours, not enough time to slog through the snow to town. Between storms he fished for food and dug out the car so it sat on a patch of spring grass amid the white.

On Monday he thought he heard a plane. On Tuesday he lit a flare and had stamped out "LL" marks in the snow when another plane flew over. The "LL" is a standard ground-to-air communication symbol that means "all well."

The weather slowly improved and the snow began to melt. He was damp and his boots sodden. Being in the car didn't help. If he opened the windows, in came the snow. If he closed them, evaporative moisture formed as though he were in a terrarium.

By Tuesday night he figured he could dash for it between weather cells.

He got up at five Wednesday morning; the snow was down to two feet. By the time he reached the valley floor, the ground was bare but muddy. Wet from six days of standing in the snow, he suffered frostbite, and to this day his feet are sensitive to the cold.

He made it to a ranch, from where he was given a ride to Leadore. Here he found the search party eating breakfast and stoking down coffee.

He walked in the cafe door and tapped the leader on the shoulder. "Ralph! Hey, just the man we've been looking for!"

Ralph called me at home, and not ten minutes later, I swear, came the call from the National Guard commander in Boise. "Mrs. Maughan?" he said, in a voice that made me think of the Normandy invasion. "We're ready to mobilize."

This entire story might be only a cautionary tale with a funny ending were it not for the event that took place later.

On July 23, 1980, two months to the day that Ralph turned up missing and three years from the date my father died, the River of No Return Wilderness bill was signed into law—2.4 million acres permanently entered into the National Wilderness Preservation System.

And it is this third and final feature that gives meaning to what came before. Without it, there's only a jumble of loss and possible loss.

I've twice been back to where my dad's ashes are scattered. It's not an easy trip—twenty-five miles of bad road over two mountain ranges, then fifteen miles and three thousand feet of elevation gain by trail. But that's exactly the point.

Certain landscapes are those of the spirit, wild and undefined. Without them, we become strangers, alien from creation, alien from the forces that give us life.

But it has taken time for me to understand the ways of mountains and mortality, distance to see random events as a whole. A massif, a literal grouping of life and death and possibility, always possibility, these wild places of the heart and of the landscape.

About the Authors

Edward Abbey pioneered the concept of the "ecowarrior" in his novel *The Monkey Wrench Gang.* He also published nineteen other books, including *Desert Solitude.* His novel *The Brave Cowboy* was made into the movie *Fire on the Mountain.* He died in 1989 at the age of sixty-two.

Donna Ashworth, a former high school English teacher, has been a fire lookout for fifteen years. Her first book, *Biography of a Small Mountain,* was published in 1991. She is presently at work on a third book. All three books are set on Woody Mountain in Arizona.

Bradley Blum has been a Bell Mountain lookout for six summers. He is a graduate of The Evergreen State College in Washington and has worked as a reporter and editor for newspapers in Alaska, Idaho, and Washington.

Drusilla Claridge lives in Silver City, New Mexico, where she has a private practice in massage and reflexology.

Sue Curtiss is the former Black Butte lookout on the Kootenai National Forest in Montana. She now works in fire management on the same forest.

Bart Eben worked his first lookout in 1949 and still staffs the Whitehawk lookout in Idaho, where he and his ex-wife honeymooned in 1966. He has long been involved with wolf studies. He has also worked in railroading and construction.

Martha Hardy was one of the first women fire lookouts in the United States and served on her post during World War II. She taught high school math until the 1970s, when she retired to Seattle.

Nomeca Hartwell has been an Oregon state fire lookout since 1989. She bought the original (circa 1920) Sexton Lookout in 1986, the same year she became keeper in charge for the National Weather Sevice at the Sexton Weather Station.

Ray Kresek is the author of *Fire Lookouts of the Northwest* and operates the Historic Lookout Project and Museum in Spokane, Washington. He has served on the board of directors of the Forest Fire Lookout Association and is a major contributor to historic lookout preservation.

Nicole LeFavour works as a community organizer and educator in Boise, Idaho. She has a master of fine arts degree in creative writing from the University of Montana and a bachelor's degree in the evolution of cognition from the University of California, Berkeley. She was a wilderness ranger for five years and a lookout for two.

Jackie Johnson Maughan has published three outdoor nonfiction books and is currently working on her second novel. She teaches English at Idaho State University, in Pocatello, and has worked as a fire lookout in Idaho and Oregon. She has been a publicist, newspaper editor, and documentary filmmaker.

Ray Obermayr is an artist, retired art professor, and writer of iconoclastic poetry.

Bud Panco first started working fires in 1945. He retired as chief of the Packwood Fire Department in 1994. He is a member of the Packwood Search and Rescue and has been the High Rock lookout since 1987.

Doug Peacock has long worked to save the grizzly bear. He is co-organizer of Round River Conservation Studies, which has sought to verify the presence of grizzlies in the San Juan Mountains in Colorado.

Don Scheese worked fire lookouts in Idaho for ten years. He is currently an assistant professor of English at Gustavus Adolphus College in St. Peter, Minnesota.

Brenda Tippin has worked as a fire lookout since 1985. She has also fought fires, done recreational patrol, cruised timber, and monitored spotted owls for the Forest Service.

Don Usner is coauthor and photographer for *The Natural History of Big Sur,* published in 1993 by the University of California Press. He has published photos in *Americas* magazine, done showings in California and Mexico, and has recently published a book on the cultural history of Chimayo.

Miles Wilson is a recipient of the John Simmons Short Fiction Award at the University of Iowa and a grant from the National Endowment for the Arts. His work has appeared in such publications as *The Georgia Review, Southwest Review,* and *New Growth: Contemporary Short Stories by Texas Writers.*

R. Lightbulb Winders was the last full-time fire lookout at Green Mountain on the Baker-Snoqualmie National Forest. He still works seasonally for the Forest Service in silviculture and fire fighting. He travels often to India and has given several photo exhibits documenting life in modern Asia.